Medic Mentor's Interview Skills Checklist UK Medical Application Guide

Practice makes medical school interviews perfect!

Preparing for medical school interviews can be overwhelming and intimidating. Each medical school has its own style and there are lots of possible interview questions.

Our Medic Mentors have put together this comprehensive medical school interview guide full of practice questions, model answers and marking templates. This will help you to understand what selectors are looking for in an exceptional candidate.

Need more help? Medic Mentor is here to support you!

Medic Mentor is a social enterprise comprised of junior doctors and medical students. We provide useful resources, advice and opportunities for aspiring medical students. We understand how challenging and confusing the medical application process can be, which is why we have created a range of resources to guide you.

We run **Interview Skills Courses** at various locations across the UK. The Part 1 course goes into detail about interview techniques, verbal and non-verbal communication skills and more. Students will have the opportunity to sit mock-panel and mock-MMI interviews with personalised feedback at the Part 2 course.

Find out more at **www.medicmentor.org**

The MASTERCLASS Guide

The MASTERCLASS guide is inspired by the MASTERCLASS courses. It is a comprehensive overview of all the topics that are taught to the MASTERCLASS students, in the years leading up to their medical school applications.

This includes the basic knowledge that students must know in order to demonstrate an insight into medicine. The guide covers the structure of the NHS, medical training, ethical principles and landmarks in Medicine and Surgery. The Guide includes notes on how to develop key skills, such as leadership, team-work, presentation, teaching and written communication. It contains guidance on study skills, time management and medical 'buzzwords' that students are expected to be familiar with. It also contains useful information about how to speak to patients and make the most of work experience.

Free for MASTERCLASS Students!

For more information on how to become a MASTERCLASS student please visit **www.medicmentor.org**

Medic Mentor®

Motivating Medical Minds

Medic Mentor's Masterclass™

The official text

UK Medical School Applications

Dhakshana Slvayoganathan

Iain Kennedy

Ciaran Kennedy

Two Other Essential Guides

Each guide addresses important aspects of the application process:

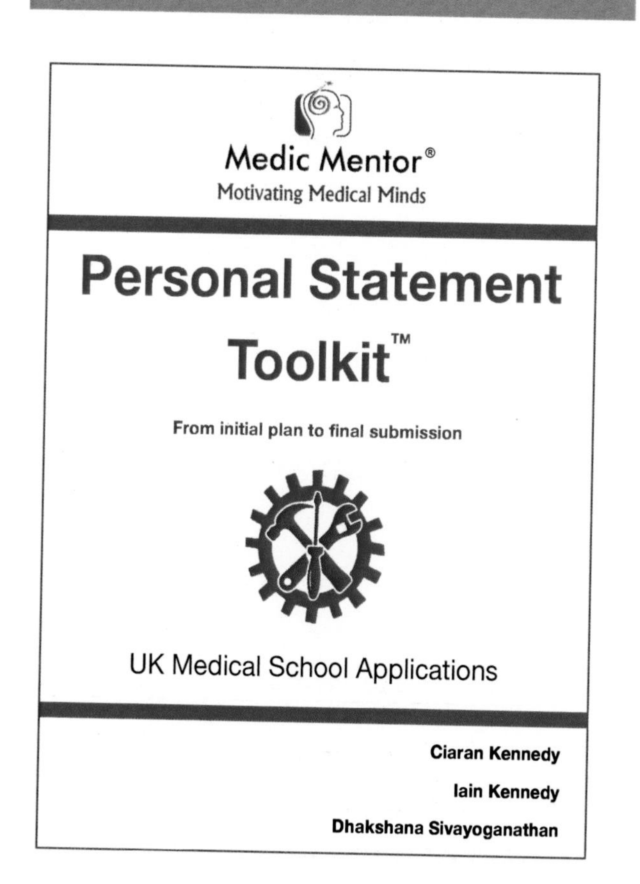

Personal Statement Toolkit

Using a wealth of experience gained from marking hundreds of personal statements, the Mentors have finally compiled all of their knowledge in this unique Personal Statement Toolkit. The guide contains mark schemes, templates, instructions and examples on how to write a statement from start to finish. The guide also includes useful timelines and writing techniques to make your statements stand out. This is a comprehensive, user-friendly guide, to help you write a statement that is unique to you!

Medical Schools Compendium

The Compendium addresses one of the most crucial and overlooked aspects of the application process: choosing the right universities to apply to. This important decision can affect the outcome of your application. This guide gives a clear breakdown of all of the UK medical schools and the facts; including competition ratios and course structures – in one place! The compendium also explains the significance of your university choices and strategies to narrow down your decision from 35 schools to just 4!

Available to order now at www.medicmentor.org or other online retailers and UK bookstores!

Contents

Published by Medic Mentor Publishing Group

Authors:
Iain Kennedy, Dhakshana Sivayoganathan, Ciaran Kennedy

Editors:
Dhakshana Sivayoganathan and Iain Kennedy

ISBN: 978-0-9569720-2-6

Medic Mentor is a registered trademark.
Website: **www.medicmentor.org**

Printed by Medic Mentor Ltd, Essex.

Purchasing any of the Medic Mentor Medical Applications Guides does not guarantee a place at medical school and it is the individual student's responsibility to submit an application via UCAS. All advice and information provided by Medic Mentor Ltd is believed to be true and accurate at the date of publication. The company cannot accept any legal responsibility or liability for any errors or omissions made. Medic Mentor Ltd makes every reasonable effort to ensure content accuracy in all of its resources. Due to the dynamic nature of medical school applications however, institutions are constantly updating their course details. To read the full disclaimer visit www.medicmentor.org/disclaimer.

Introduction

Aims and objectives of this medical application guide

The medical school interview is one the most stressful and confusing parts of the application process. Almost all medical schools interview for places, but this process can vary greatly between institutions. We receive a lot of questions about how to prepare for medical school interviews at our events. This guide focuses specifically on these issues.

Aims and objectives of the Interview Skills Checklists

Aim 1 – *question identification*

1) To provide an extensive list of typical medical school interview questions.
2) To separate these questions into genres and similar topics for ease of study.
3) To group similar questions together to make answering these questions easier for the student.
4) To identify questions that, initially look similar, but are actually different and require different approaches when providing answers. These are referred to as 'curveball questions'.

Aim 2 – *theoretical advice*

1) To clarify what questions are actually asking – what do they really want to know?
2) To highlight what questions are not asking – what they do not want to know.
3) To describe how to link underlying skills and attributes with examples.
4) To recommend medical 'buzzwords' that will strengthen your answers.

Aim 3 – *worked examples*

1) To provide typical and realistic answers, representative of students at your level.

2) To structure these answers logically according to 'easy-to-replicate' systems you can follow.
3) To demonstrate how your skills, learning points and reflections should be placed in order.
4) To stimulate you to think about your own experiences and how they compare to our examples.

Aim 4 – *your answers and marking checklists*

1) To provide you with space to record your own 'model' answers and allow you to practice them.
2) To provide you with typical medical-school-like mark schemes, so that you can test yourself.
3) To demonstrate the need to include all the relevant points, in order to 'tick the boxes'.
4) To help you realise that interviews are positively marked, information gathering processes only.

Aim 5 – *continuing support*

Medic Mentor has a strong presence online and on social media. This is how we communicate with many of our students and parents, and we welcome queries from anyone and everyone. Often we receive similar questions time and again and we are more than happy to answer these. It only takes a minute to post or email us a question and the answer may be simpler than you thought. Occasionally, your questions may require more time or discussion with specific institutions. We regularly communicate with medical schools and would be happy to research a more complicated issue on your behalf.

Please contact us at: admin@medicmentor.org *or* Facebook.com/medicmentor

Part 1: Before You Apply

Important factors affecting your application

Applying to medicine is a multifactorial decision; other than interviews there are lots of different factors that you need to consider before making your application to your chosen institutions. Below is a short list of the major factors that will influence your application to medical school, other than interviews. These issues (and many more) are covered specifically in the ***Making it into Medicine*** course and in the ***Medical Schools Compendium (MSC)***. They will not be dwelt upon here except where they relate directly to common interview questions. More information on these resources can be found at www.medicmentor.org. It is also a good idea to attend open days for the universities you are going to apply to. This will give you some insight into many of the areas listed below.

Entry requirements

Every school has minimum academic grades for application eligibility. They also state mandatory subject combinations, and subjects that do not count. This information is essential pre-application reading and can be found in university prospectuses, websites and the MSC. You should also be aware of medical school entry examinations. These include the UKCAT, BMAT and GMASAT (post-grad). There are a small minority of medical school courses that do not require you to sit an entrance exam. Information can be found in the previously mentioned resources.

Institution location and setting

Universities vary greatly in their settings. Some are out-of-town campus universities and others are integrated city universities. There are also mixtures of the two. You should visit all of the institutions that you are applying to, because you are going to be living there for at least 5 years. This will give you the opportunity to work out other issues such as how far you will be from friends and family, what the accommodation options are and whether you actually like the place you are applying to. This last point is key because if you are happy in your environment you will enjoy yourself more and probably do much better in your studies. Finally, you can expect institution specific questions at interview and it always looks good if you have some background knowledge about the university. A good idea is to list your reasons for wanting to study at your chosen medical schools. A really common question after, "why medicine?" is, "why this university?" The MSC is really good at providing you with the information to answer these questions.

Teaching curricula

Nowadays, most medical schools market themselves as having an 'integrated curriculum'. This generally refers to the integration of basic sciences and clinical topics, or university based teaching and real patient contact. In reality, all universities exist on a spectrum when it comes to their curricula. More traditional universities will favour a didactic approach i.e. lectures and formal teaching sessions. These centres also tend to have more of a separation between early pre-clinical a clinical years. They also tend to utilise distinct subject-based teaching topics, such as biochemistry, cell biology and histopathology. In later years, subjects are normally split into systems such as cardiovascular or the nervous system. You are more likely to find full-body-dissection in these institutions and probably later patient contact.

More modern styled universities tend to utilise a problem-based learning (PBL) approach to their curricula. This tends to involve less 'contact time' (or time spent) in university, and more independent and small group study. The emphasis here is more upon students doing their own research around topics and across multiple subjects. Teachers act more as facilitators rather than speakers and are arguably more available to individual students. You are less likely to find large lectures in these institutions and more likely to find earlier patient contact.

Differences in medical school curricula are also important, as they will influence the questions asked at interview. Traditional schools classically favour evidence of academic excellence whereas PBL courses often look for skills fundamental to effective independent study. There are a lot of overlaps here but if you can demonstrate familiarity with medical school curricula – specifically the schools you are applying to –

then you will look very good at interview; you will seem like you have made a more informed decision to study medicine.

Ultimately, each institution is special and unique in its own way. It is important for you to know why *you* want to go there, because it will make answering these questions much easier and more sincere.

Competition ratios

Another area to be familiar with is the statistics – how many people apply for a place at your chosen medical school each year. Information can be difficult to come by and is not always listed in university prospectuses. This information is useful when making application choices but it should also be appreciated in its context. There are lots of factors that affect medical school competition ratios and you should seek to understand these rather than taking the numbers at face value. In addition to this, competition ratios change every year; sometimes swinging massively. Again if you familiarise yourself with some of the underlying factors, you may understand why. This topic is analysed in detail on the *Making it into Medicine* course. Below is a list of some factors that can influence competition ratios:

- ✓ Academic entry requirements including yearly changes and prospectus updates,
- ✓ Medical entrance exams and changing decisions from medical schools on which they use,
- ✓ The age of the university, its traditions and sub-cultures,
- ✓ Current league table rankings and international research ratings,
- ✓ Student union rankings and National Union of Students (NUS) reviews,
- ✓ Previous years' competition ratios,
- ✓ Other press-related issues that make universities more or less popular,
- ✓ The location or city the university is in and changes here (e.g. new shopping centres or social attractions),
- ✓ Transport links – buses, trains and planes,
- ✓ Costs and available student finance or funding options for this area,
- ✓ Scholarships and widening access to medical school initiatives,

✓ Local or related medical foundation and access courses.

What you should know about medical school interviews before you apply

1. *Why do medical schools interview?*

If you think about it, everything that medical schools know about you before the interview is contained in a few words and numbers written on a page. A well-written personal statement, supported by a good reference and an excellent set of grades, gives them a minor insight into who you really are. Therefore, most institutions require an interview process to gather additional information, check facts and use this opportunity to meet you in person. They want to see a demonstration of your skills and compare this to their requirements for a typical medical student. They will also be on the look out for any negative traits that might prevent you from being a good doctor.

Generally speaking, by the time you have reached the interview, the selectors have decided that you are capable of meeting the demands of their medical degree. They are now looking to recruit the *best* candidates. In order to demonstrate this you need to possess an excellent interview style. You also need to look professional and competent by:

✓ Knowing your personal statement like the back of your hand and be prepared to elaborate on your experiences,
✓ Having additional examples of skills, experiences and reflections that you can draw upon,
✓ Practising to use medical buzzwords and phrases and know how they relate to your own skills,
✓ Reading 'Tomorrow's Doctors', 'Modernising Medical Careers' and some topical NHS articles,
✓ Having a basic grasp of fundamental medical ethics, law and some landmark cases,
✓ Practising interview questions extensively before you get to your interview.

2. *Traditional versus MMI – what's the difference?*

Medical school interviews typically use two main formats. These are 'traditional panel interviews' and 'multiple mini interviews' (MMI). The differences between these are not huge. However, certain topics can be assessed in different ways depending on the interview style.

During traditional panel interviews, candidates are interviewed by the same interviewers, in the same room; from start to finish. This form of interview is longer; anywhere from 20 to 45 minutes. There can be a variable number of people in the room and normally there is a good mix of junior and senior professionals. Typically the number is between two and four interviewers and you might even find a medical student, an observer or a non-medical interviewer present. This type of interview takes the form of an extended conversation that is split into different sections. Interviewers normally take turns to answer questions and they usually focus on different attributes (e.g. work experience, transferrable skills or extracurricular achievements). Applicants who do well in traditional interviews are those who can develop rapport with multiple speakers and who have a good command of the English language.

MMIs are an evolution of the interview process. They are relatively new in undergraduate medicine but have been used in other disciplines for years. They can be thought of as a traditional interview that has been split up into several stations for separate assessable attributes. They also mimic the Objective Structured Clinical Examinations (OSCEs), used to test practical skills in medical students and doctors. One major advantage of MMIs is that each station feels like a new leaf and if you did not do well in the previous station, you have a new set of assessors. Some stations do not even require you to speak (e.g. written communication stations) and this potentially removes the bias towards well-spoken students. This style also enables practical skills to be tested; for example counselling and empathy stations focus specifically on your verbal communication. An added advantage of these stations is that skills being tested are often clearly signposted. For example, the instructions may state that this is a 'verbal communication station'. To this end some students prefer MMIs as they are arguably less ambiguous and it may be easier to tell what the examiner is looking for.

What to expect in the interview

You should expect the specific format listed on the medical school prospectus. It is important to find this out prior to applying as interview format 'fashions' change yearly. Whether your interview is an MMI or the more traditional approach, you can expect broadly the same topics to arise. These have been listed below:

- ✓ Questions or stations regarding your motivation to study medicine,
- ✓ Questions or stations to test your knowledge and understanding of medical training,
- ✓ Questions or stations to test your knowledge and understanding of the specific medical school,
- ✓ Questions or stations to test background medical knowledge, and wider medical interests,
- ✓ Questions or stations to assess your work experience reflections and insight into a medical career,
- ✓ Questions or stations to assess your transferrable skills and desirable attributes for a future doctor,
- ✓ Questions or stations relating to your extracurricular activities, well roundedness and stress relief,
- ✓ Questions or stations relating to socio-cultural awareness, community involvement, caring and charity,
- ✓ Questions or stations to test your understanding of modern medicine and topical NHS issues,
- ✓ Questions or stations to test your knowledge of medical ethics and basic healthcare legislation,
- ✓ Questions or stations aimed more at graduate students,
- ✓ Questions or stations more specific to Oxbridge students.

Topics that translate well into MMI stations have been listed below. All of the topics above and below will be addressed in Part 3 of this book, with worked examples, explanations and detailed marking checklists for you to practice with.

- ✓ **Written communication MMI station** – answering questions often without an invigilator present,
- ✓ **Verbal communication station** – demonstrating counselling and empathy skills with an actor,
- ✓ **Personal statement station** – answering questions relating to your statement,
- ✓ **Situational judgement testing** – making decisions with limited information using best practice,
- ✓ **Comprehension station** – interpreting written information and answering verbal questions,
- ✓ **Critical appraisal station** – critically analysing data with written or verbal questions,
- ✓ **Presentation station** – presenting a topic at short notice to an invigilator,
- ✓ **Moral reasoning station** – discussing an ethical situation and deciding on best practice,
- ✓ **Problem solving station** – dealing with a medical or non-medical issue and making decisions.

What happens in the interview room?

The situations are similar in the panel interview and MMI rooms. If you are seated, place both feet on the ground; lean forward slightly and make appropriate eye contact with anyone who addresses you. Try to keep your body language open and your hands on display. Do not fiddle or fidget and try your best to smile. This is a high-pressure environment but try to enjoy yourself as much as you can. Making it to the interview stage is an achievement in itself. The likelihood is that the medical school already wants you, so think positive be open and honest and don't give them a reason not to offer you a place. For more information on improving your interview technique, Medic Mentor runs a regular **Interview Skills Courses** throughout the UK. Information is available on the website www.medicmentor.org.

Part 2: Answering questions effectively

How to structure your answer to different questions

In the last section, we mentioned some major interview question topics. Now we will go on to discuss how you can address questions in a logical manner, make clear points and provide evidence for these points. Firstly, it is helpful to look at the interview as a whole and the lasting impression you want to leave with the selectors. We have already described interviews as an information gathering process and we have consistently talked about 'mark schemes' and 'checklists' being used by selectors. In order to get all of the marks, you need to craft your answers so that they make it really clear to the interviewers that you have what they are looking for in each section. Below is a list of the 10 main points you need to get across in your questions:

1. You have a genuine interest in medicine and have developed a realistic insight into the profession.
2. You have gained this insight from relevant work experience.
3. You have identified the transferrable skills and desirable attributes of a doctor.
4. You have evidence to support the development of these skills and attributes in yourself.
5. You appreciate the holistic, patient-centred and caring nature of medicine.
6. You can demonstrate both academic and extracurricular evidence.
7. You can formulate arguments and actively reflect upon your learning.
8. You are aware of current political and topical NHS issues and its effect upon healthcare.
9. You are a balanced human being with the capacity for hard work and the ability to deal with stress.
10. You work effectively with all people and groups, irrespective of their background or level of education.

Other challenges arise in interviews when questions are asked in different ways. This can be confusing, as you have to take time to analyse questions and work out exactly what the interviewer is looking for. Do refer back to the points above because the likelihood is that most questions (no matter how convoluted they may seem), are simply an attempt to stimulate you into making one of the generic points above. In general if you are thinking too hard about a question then you have probably missed the point and you should ask the interviewers to rephrase the question. This takes up a little time but it is good practice as you may be given a much simpler question alluding to the same generic points. You do not lose points for asking for clarification – if it is done tactfully it can actually be an example of good communication skills.

Point, evidence and explanation (PEE) - questions asking for examples

Essentially, all interview questions are indirectly asking you to 'tick the box' on an interviewer's mark scheme. They cannot say that; so instead they ask for examples, experiences and reflections that would demonstrate the point clearly. This is why many questions open with phrases such as, "give me an example of" or, "tell me about a time when you demonstrated" or perhaps "what do you know about [something topical] and how have gone about preparing yourself for such an event?" You can see that all of these questions, and indeed the majority of interview questions relate to recalling past examples. The interviewers want you to provide them with evidence. They require you to use this evidence to make a point. You should then explain the link between your evidence, the point you are making and how it all links up with you being an appropriate candidate for medicine. Here is a worked example of the whole question and answer process:

Question: Give me an example of when you demonstrated good team-working and communication skills.

The 'point' has actually been made for you here in the question – communication and team-working skills are important.

Answer: "I demonstrated these skills effectively when I took part in a team assent to Everest Base Camp in Year 11".

In this opening section, you have provided the interviewer with a specific example or piece of 'evidence'.

Answer (continued): "I was responsible for organising my teammates into buddy pairs, monitoring their hydration and looking for signs of altitude sickness. I communicated this information to our lead teacher and the team medic".

The continuation of your answer is important in order to develop the example and make it more credible.

Answer (continued): "I feel that the skills I utilised here are highly applicable to a career in medicine, in particular when communicating patient observations and trends to senior doctors on ward rounds".

This concluding part of the answer comprises the 'explanation'. This is where the link to medicine is made clear, as is the significance of your experience, reflection and skill development. This answer also hints at further medical experience. It is a good skill if you are able to do this, as it might direct the questioning towards a topic that you feel comfortable discussing. For example, here the interviewer has been prompted to ask more about where you have seen doctors communicating in clinical settings or on ward rounds.

More open-ended or ambiguous questions

Sometimes interviewers like to leave things more open-plan and allow you to fill the void with your own answers. A typical question here might be, "tell me about your work experience". Clearly this is more of a request than a question. There is however a question that lives in the subtext:

"Do you have a good example of work experience which you have reflected upon? Have you analysed the underlying transferrable skills, developed these and demonstrated how this experience makes you well prepared to study medicine?"

Or to put it more simply:

"I have these boxes on my mark sheet that say: 'evidence of relevant work experience' and 'development of transferrable skills applicable to medicine'. Can you help me tick them in less than two minutes?"

Remember the interview is about providing information. Lay your **points** out clearly, support them with **evidence** and briefly **explain** the link to medicine.

'I believe I will make a good doctor because I have good team-working and communication skills ***(point)****. I demonstrated these when I took part in a team assent to Everest Base Camp in Year 11* ***(evidence)****. I was responsible for organising my teammates into buddy pairs, monitoring their hydration and looking for signs of altitude sickness. I communicated this information to our lead teacher and the team medic. I feel that the communication and team working skills I utilised here are highly applicable to a career in medicine, in particular when communicating patient observations and trends to senior doctors on ward rounds* ***(explanation)****.'*

If you study subjects that require lots of essays, such as history or English literature, you may have come across other logical systems for structuring answers to questions. One such system is Borton's model. Instead of, 'point, evidence, explanation', Borton advocates the use of, 'what? So what? Now what?' Some people find this model more intuitive when answering questions on the spot. For those of you looking for a comprehensive system of logical reflection, Medic Mentor suggests Gibbs' reflective cycle. This well established model is actually integrated into the NHS ePortfolio system and many of the interviewers will recognise it. By utilising Gibbs, you force yourself to reflect more comprehensively than with either PEE or Borton. The downside however is that Gibbs' model takes longer to implement and you can sometimes miss a step or get confused halfway through your answer. For this reason Medic Mentor tends to suggest

Gibbs' model for personal statements, where you have time to craft more detailed written answers. Below is a table that combines all of the above-mentioned logical systems (including another one called STARR). It is up to you which model suits your individual style. You may even use a combination of all of them. It does not really matter how you achieve this, provided that you can get your points across and tick the boxes,

Gibbs' Reflective Cycle *Gibbs 1988*	Description >> Feelings >> Evaluation >> Analysis >> Conclusions >> Actions
STARR	Situation >> Task >> Action >> Result >> Relate
Borton's Model	What? >> Now what? >> So what?
PEE Don't forget to PEE	Point >> Evidence >> Explanation

Interview situations that require you to engage with a scenario

Some interview questions relate to a scenario that you are given. This tends to be the case with ethical, moral or medico-legal type questions. You will find that instead of being asked to reflect upon your own experiences, you are required to apply your knowledge and skills to a new (hypothetical) situation. It is important that you have a basic grasp of medical ethics. It would also be helpful to know about some basic healthcare legislation and a few landmark cases. This is an area where additional knowledge makes you stand out and also makes answering these questions easier. Many ethical scenarios, for example, may resemble famous cases that you have read about.

These scenarios also tend to lend themselves well to Gibbs' cycle, the only difference being that they are hypothetical instead of retrospective. In other words, these situations are fictional as opposed to something that really happened to you. A good example of such a situation would be 'a consultant who arrives on the ward smelling of alcohol and acting strangely'. Let us now apply Gibbs' cycle here:

Description >> Feelings >> Evaluation >> Analysis >> Conclusions >> Actions

The description is given to you in the scenario. It is then down to you to discuss how it makes you feel. Most of us would feel uncomfortable with a senior colleague under the influence of alcohol, especially as this is somebody whom we would normally go to for senior advice. Beware of limited information in these scenarios, as they are typical pitfalls that some people miss. In addition to following a model of logical deduction, you need to identify alternative explanations or arguments for events. It is by exploring multiple options and explaining your logic that gets you marks for your ability to 'problem-solve'. Interviewers are not mind readers; they need to hear your thought processes 'out loud'. The final piece of the puzzle is referring to ethical, legal and professional principles. For example:

"I would feel worried by this situation, as there is a chance that my senior colleague may be under the influence of alcohol **(feelings)**. This is bad **(evaluation)** as he has a duty of care **(professional responsibility)** to his patients and may not be able to deliver this to the best of his ability if he is drunk **(analysis).** He may also do harm to his patients **(ethico-legal principle)** by giving them poor treatment. This situation puts patient safety at risk **(conclusion and professional responsibility)**. Therefore I would want to bring the issue to the attention of somebody who can deal with things appropriately **(action)"**.

At this point you have scored most of the marks as you have highlighted the major issues. You could signpost the uncertainty by saying, "I would check with colleagues to see if anybody else had noticed the issue". This lets them know that you are open-minded and that when you are unsure, you ask for help – the safe thing to do. You may also be asked about whom you would inform on the ward. This is tricky for students who have not done hospital work experience as they might not know how things work. In general, the trick with these situations is to do whatever is safest and what does the least harm to patients and staff – Remember that you have a duty of care to the Trust, your colleagues and to patients. Essentially though, it is about how you justify your answers that counts, not necessarily what you say you would do. For example you could say any of the following and still get points:

"In order to maintain patient safety, I would contact security immediately and have the offending doctor removed from the ward". **A logical but excessive action to take.**

"In order to maintain patient safety I would go straight to the senior ward sister and ask her to deal with the issue appropriately". **This demonstrates understanding of ward responsibility but could be harmful to the doctor, as the issue has been escalated outside of his discipline.**

"I would seek to clarify the situation with my immediate seniors and look for corroboration of my opinions. We would then go as a group to the next most senior doctor on the ward and present our concerns discretely and away from the patient environment. We would discuss with this doctor, the most confidential and appropriate way to deal with the issue without alarming patients or other members of the healthcare team. It would then be the responsibility of the remaining senior doctor to arrange cover for the consultant so that no patients come to harm and the ward round could continue". **This example is a bit long-winded but it clearly shows insight, compassion and professionalism. It suggests that you can prioritise issues according to seriousness, remain objective in a difficult situation and that you know how to work as part of a team.**

We will go through some more worked examples of ethical-type scenarios in the next section of this guide. You can also find detailed explanations of ethical principles in the MASTERCLASS guide.

Situational judgement testing (SJT)

This is a relatively new concept in medical school interviews. It has been widely used in postgraduate selection and from there it has 'trickled down' into final year medical students' foundation programme applications. SJTs can now be found as both MMI stations and in dedicated sections of traditional panel interviews. The good thing about SJTs is that they are not all that different from ethical, moral or medico-legal scenarios, which have been used in undergraduate selection for a while now.

Where SJTs tend to differ slightly is in their specific execution and marking. There is no free-form approach where you are asked to comment generally upon the issues involved. Instead, you will be presented with a limited range of actions to take, and you will then be required to pick an option and justify it. You should approach all SJTs with an open mind and expect to have very little information upon which to base your decisions. You have to work with what you have and you are not allowed to ask for more information.

Your reasoning should be spoken out loud similar any scenario that asks for proposed actions. You will be awarded points for choosing the best option but also for logical reasoning and demonstrating that you are safe, sensible and that you have carefully considered all of the options. The majority of SJTs can be easily reasoned if you apply the basic ethical principles of **autonomy, beneficence, non-maleficence and justice.**

Ethical and moral reasoning, situational judgement and basic research methods are covered in detail as part of Medic Mentor's MASTERCLASS courses, which take places regularly across the UK. For more information please visit www.medicmentor.org.

There will be some examples of SJTs in the next section of this guide, complete with easy theoretical breakdowns and learning points.

Part 3: Interview skills checklists: **Panel Interview & MMI**

Medic Mentor's Part 1 Interview Skills Course runs at various locations across the UK. Students and parents are very welcome to attend. Registration is £45 and includes a course workbook and attendance certificate. Visit www.medicmentor.org to register and find courses near you.

The course will help you to:

- ✓ Build confidence in your communications skills.
- ✓ Discuss topical questions that are likely to come up in the interview.
- ✓ Learn about non-verbal communications skills.
- ✓ Avoid common mistakes.
- ✓ Learn skills from experienced lecturers and successful applicants.

Interview questions: motivation to study medicine

Typical interview questions that come under this topic

- ✓ Why medicine?
- ✓ When did you decide medicine was for you?
- ✓ How did you come to your decision to study medicine?
- ✓ How have you developed your interest in this career?
- ✓ What have you done to find out about a career in medicine?
- ✓ How informed is your decision to pursue a career in medicine?

Example question and answer from our mentors

Question: *How did you come to your decision to study medicine?*

Answer: *At school I really enjoyed human biology but it wasn't until a doctor came to speak at our school, that I really started to think about medicine as a career. I developed my initial interest by arranging work experience in a GP practice and on a stroke ward. I wanted to learn more about the career and to test my own suitability for medicine. I observed doctors dealing with many difficult situations including communicating with patients who have chronic diseases and counselling patients who could no longer speak following a stroke. I now understand that being a doctor requires a lot of non-scientific and transferrable skills. I have practised these through acting classes and my roles as a prefect and junior student mentor. Academically, I have the grades for medicine. In addition to this I have developed an insight into the career and worked hard to make myself a well-rounded applicant.*

What they want to know

When and where you came across the concept of a career in medicine. How you have developed this initial interest via work experience and the acquisition of transferrable skills. How these experiences have helped you to make a logical conclusion: that medicine is the right career for you.

What you need to say

Detail the time and place your interest was first kindled. Mention how you were stimulated to learn more. Describe how you arranged work experience to expose yourself to the medical working environment. Briefly comment upon some skills you identified and why you feel the career might be a good fit for you. Conclude with a clear message that your decision is personal, well informed and based upon detailed reflection from high quality experience.

What not to say

Do not fabricate or exaggerate the origins of your medical interests. It does not matter where your interest in medicine stemmed from. It is your development of this interest through experience and the acquisition of transferrable skills that matters. Be clear and avoid ambiguous phrases such as, 'I have always wanted to do medicine.'

'Curveballs' and challenging follow-up questions

- ✓ Why not nursing as they arguably have more patient contact?
- ✓ Why not work for an international charity because they help more people?
- ✓ Why don't you become a politician as they are better placed to exact social change?
- ✓ Why not pharmacy if you enjoyed your work experience there?
- ✓ What would you like to contribute to the field of medicine?

What they are actually asking

How well do you know the basics of what a job in medicine entails? Do you have a varied set of work experiences that have given you enough insight into medicine to make a reasonably informed career choice? Do you appreciate the differences between medicine and other careers? Have you considered other options and made a justifiable decision to be a doctor instead of another profession?

Example question and answer from our mentors

Question: *Why not nursing instead?*

Answer: *I did look into a career in nursing and I spent many hours shadowing nurses on my work experience in hospitals and at a GP practice. I appreciate that they often have more patient contact but there are a lot of things I could not do as a nurse. These include becoming a surgeon, anaesthetist or other specialist doctor. I enjoy the clinical problem-solving, challenging situations and responsibility that doctors experience. I also want to have the ability to make decisions about possible treatments. As a nurse, I would have limited opportunities for further academic study unless I did an additional degree. Ever since my work experience when I observed an appendicectomy; I have been fascinated by surgery. A career in nursing would not allow me to develop this interest into a career aspiration.*

Your turn – write your answer here

Question: *Why is medicine the career for you?*

Answer:

Interview Skills Checklist (inspired by university mark schemes)

Assessment Areas	Very poor	Poor	Below average	Average	Above average	Very good	Excellent	Points
Credible origin of medical career interest								
Clear evidence of career interest development via work experience								
Identifies specific skills transferrable to medicine								
Evidence of personal skill development								
Realistic insight into medical career								
Overall quality of reflections								

Points total	Percentage Score	Passing score
/42	%	**>80% *or* 34/42**

Rating	Very poor	Poor	Below average	Average	Above average	Very good	Excellent
Points awarded	**1**	**2**	**3**	**4**	**5**	**6**	**7**

Interview questions: knowledge and understanding of medical training

Typical interview questions that come under this topic

- ✓ What do you know about the structure of medical training?
- ✓ What do you know about the differences between postgraduate specialty training routes?
- ✓ How long does it take to become a consultant?
- ✓ How long will it take to become a doctor?

Example question and answer from our mentors

Question: *How long does it take to become a consultant?*

Answer: *On my work experience in a large teaching hospital, I got the chance to speak to a lot of doctors from different specialties. I asked them all about their training pathways and I found out that there are a few different routes to becoming a consultant. Apart from five years at medical school (six for some courses and intercalaters), everyone has to do a two-year foundation programme. Doctors can then split off into core medicine or core surgery (for two years), or GP training (which is three years currently but may become longer by the time I get there). I'm currently interested in ophthalmology as a career and I know it would take at least 14 years from where I am now to become a consultant. I will most likely intercalate though and I know many senior doctors do travelling fellowship years after ST7 – making it at least 16 years. Alternatively I could be a GP in less than 10 years. I want to explore all of my options during medical school and I will make a more informed decision from there.*

What they want to know

In this section the interviewers are looking for some specific knowledge of the training structures. They essentially want to know that you are aware of the long and variable training pathway from undergraduate to postgraduate medicine. Again, they are keen to see evidence of your own research in this area and some indication that you are making an informed career decision.

What you need to say

You need to detail what you know about the training structure. You will look impressive if you can comment on any proposed changes or topical issues that may affect training in the future. If you are particularly interested in a medical specialty, make sure that you know its basic training structure. You can expect this as a follow up question if you talk about specific specialty aspirations. Also be aware of generic undergraduate training programme features such as electives and intercalated degrees.

What not to say

You cannot be vague in this section. Not knowing about the foundation programme, core-training or run-through training makes it look like your career choice is not well informed.

'Curveballs' and challenging follow-up questions

- ✓ What do you know about academic medicine?
- ✓ What do you know about the planned changes to GP training?
- ✓ Have you considered an intercalated degree?

What they are actually asking

These questions are quite specific and are designed to test how much reading you have done into a medical career. They also probe into your knowledge of the institution. For example, your chosen university may have a history of academic prowess and actually offer an MB PhD degree (i.e. an intercalated 3 years to complete a full PhD alongside a medical degree). Again it all comes back down to informed career decisions.

Example question and answer from our mentors

Question: *What do you know about the planned changes to GP training?*

Answer: *In lower 6th form I spent a week shadowing in a GP surgery. I enjoyed learning about the daily jobs a GP does and some of the challenges that they face. I also had the opportunity to talk to my GP about a career in medicine. He told me about how he studied at university and intercalated in medical education as a BSc. From there he continued his research in medical education through an academic foundation programme, during which he got a journal publication. I told my GP that I am interested in teaching and research. He advised me to look into GP as a career and this was when I came across some academic GP training programmes with a mixture of research and clinical training. These are four years at present but I read that GP training may be increasing. I know there is a shortage of GPs and the government is trying to attract more doctors into general practice. During my work experience, I have seen how being a GP works well with other commitments – my GP has 4 children and enjoys his weekends. Overall, I think being a GP would be a satisfying career but I am still interested in surgery and anaesthetics and I would like to explore these more during my time at medical school.*

Your turn – write your answer here

Question: *What do you know about the differences between postgraduate specialty training routes?*

Answer:

Interview Skills Checklist (inspired by university mark schemes)

Assessment Areas	Very poor	Poor	Below average	Average	Above average	Very good	Excellent	Points
Demonstrates knowledge of medical training structure								
Clear evidence of background research into medicine								
Knowledge of current affairs affecting training								
Evidence of clinical experience to inform decisions								
Identification and development of transferrable skills								
Overall quality of reflections								

Points total	Percentage Score	Passing score
/42	%	>80% *or* 34/42

Rating	Very poor	Poor	Below average	Average	Above average	Very good	Excellent
Points awarded	1	2	3	4	5	6	7

Interview questions: knowledge and understanding of specific medical school

Typical interview questions that come under this topic

- ✓ Why this medical school?
- ✓ What specific course features made you apply to this university?
- ✓ What do you know about our PBL-based curriculum?
- ✓ What do you think about our integrated curriculum?
- ✓ What do you think about our traditional approach to medical education?
- ✓ What is the best feature of our medical school?
- ✓ Why is our course better suited to you than others?

Example question and answer from our mentors

Questions: *Why is our course better suited to you than others?*

Answer: *I applied to the* [insert medical school here] *for a number of reasons. Firstly, I think the mixture of self-directed study, problem-based learning and some formal lectures will really contribute to my personal learning style. I think having information delivered to you in a lecture is great but I also thrive when I am given access to resources and allowed to study in my own way. I also know that part of this integrated course involves full body dissection. This was a major pull factor for me as I am a 'hands-on' learner and I have a current career interest in surgery that I would like to develop through anatomy and clinical attachments in surgery. Lastly, I know your curriculum has recently changed to incorporate earlier patient contact so that we get one morning a week on the ward or in a GP. This is really important to me because I decided to be a doctor so that I can work with people every day – not just learn about how they work and how to fix them.*

What they want to know

Having broad knowledge is important but at some point the obvious question will arise – why this institution? You need to demonstrate that you have made an informed decision to attend their particular medical school as you are going to be there for five or more years. The selectors are also subtly probing to see how you can contribute to their school – academically and otherwise. You also need to make the point that you are well rounded and have interests outside of medicine. These suggest that you are more sustainable and more likely to deal well with the stress of medical studies.

What you need to say

Let them know what attracts you to the city, the university and the curriculum. Talk about PBL versus the traditional approach, intercalation opportunities, elective opportunities, open days you went to, staff members or students you have spoken to, summer schools you have attended and extracurricular opportunities offered by the university. Show them that you have spent time researching the university and be specific about your plans to engage academically, socially and with extracurricular activities.

What not to say

Do not waste time telling the selectors things they already know. You also do not need to go into detail about other institutions – that is missing the point. Additionally, statements such as, 'this is the best university in the world' are unjustified and unhelpful.

'Curveballs' and challenging follow-up questions

- ✓ What could you offer our Medical School?
- ✓ Why should we choose you instead of any of the other applicants today?

What they are actually asking

Sometimes the selectors push a bit harder or are more specific with their questions. In your answers to the previous questions one of the main points should have been 'what **you** could offer the school'. If you have not made this clear, they may ask you more directly (as above), and you should still be able to get the marks if you answer it well. Other follow-up question can appear a bit mean at first (such as the second curveball question). Clearly you will never know what other applicants have to offer and it is a good idea to mention this. You should then proceed to answer the question similarly to the first one above. Remember medical interviews are information-gathering processes. Tricky sounding questions are not there to trip you up. Instead they are designed to stimulate you to reflect upon your own experiences and attributes, resulting in more detailed answers.

Example question and answer from our mentors

Question: *Why should we choose you instead of any of the other applicants today?*

Answer: *Well I can't speak for any other applicant, but I can tell you why I think I would make a good addition to your Medical School. I have explored medicine through varied work experience placements where I learned the importance of empathetic doctor-patient relationships in effective patient care. I appreciate the importance of medical ethics; I have scientific writing experience, and a fascination for public health. I have excelled in extracurricular activities, representing my school in rugby, and effectively balancing work commitments with social activities. I have developed leadership, team-working and teaching skills, and I seek to further these through a medical career. Ultimately, I feel prepared to study medicine and I would welcome the opportunity to pursue my chosen career path.*

Your turn – write your answer here

Question: *What specific course features made you apply to this university?*

Answer:

Interview Skills Checklist (inspired by university mark schemes)

Assessment Areas	Very poor	Poor	Below average	Average	Above average	Very good	Excellent	Points
Demonstrates knowledge of the medical school and curriculum								
Demonstrates skills and ability to balance commitments								
Evidence to suggest positive contribution to institution								
Evidence of sustainability and balanced lifestyle								
Realistic insight into medical career								
Overall quality of reflections								

Points total	Percentage Score	Passing score
/42	%	**>80% *or* 34/42**

Rating	Very poor	Poor	Below average	Average	Above average	Very good	Excellent
Points awarded	**1**	**2**	**3**	**4**	**5**	**6**	**7**

Typical interview questions that come under this topic

- ✓ Tell me about an area of medicine or science that interests you.
- ✓ Tell me about a science topic that you enjoyed at school.
- ✓ Which organ system do you find to be the most interesting?
- ✓ Tell me about a disease that interest you.
- ✓ Tell me about an important event in medical history.

Example question and answer from our mentors

Question: Tell me about a disease that interest you

Answer: *During my GP placement, I saw a lot of patients with diabetes. Some had type 1 and required regular insulin monitoring, blood sugars and HBa1C tests. There were also other patients with type 2 who were using a mixture of tablets, diet control and insulin. I know that type 2 diabetes in particular is increasing in incidence and prevalence in the developed world, and is closely linked to diet and lifestyle. What I never really appreciated is that both type 1 and type 2 have serious effects upon the eyes, kidneys and nerves. I saw many patients with neuropathy in the practice nurse's foot clinic, and many others were sent to eye casualty with bleeds in the backs of their eyes. In GCSE and A-level biology, I learned about the pancreas, the islets of Langerhans and basic glucose metabolism. On reflection it is easy to forget about the human cost of disease. My GP placement helped me to put some of my scientific learning into a human context and this is exactly why I want to be a doctor.*

What they want to know

Interviewers want to know that you have delved deeper into the world of medicine and science. Studying medicine involves absorbing a lot of scientific information but also appreciating it's 'real world context'. It is important to demonstrate academic ability, but this is well covered by your academic grades. Doing some background reading on a subject that interests you is really good evidence for self-directed study. This is an important skill in exam revision and particularly for problem-based learning courses.

What you need to say

Pick a topic and give some basic scientific background to demonstrate your wider reading on the subject. This is a time-limited situation so you will not have time to go into much detail. It will look great if you can make links to your work experience and tie it all to your aspiration for a career in medicine. Try to deliver your answer like a story, in a chronological way. This helps you to 'sign-post' your interests and show how your work experience and your background reading are the development of these interests. You can then make the link to medicine by showing it as logical endpoint following all of your research and experiences (and transferrable skills development).

What not to say

Try not to list lots of scientific information without reflecting or explaining the link to a career in medicine. You can go into more detail if you can make links to how your learning will make you a better candidate for medicine – this is always the underlying issue that needs addressing.

'Curveballs' and challenging follow-up questions

- ✓ What is the most important discovery in modern medicine?
- ✓ Who is the most important figure in the history of medicine?

What they are actually asking

These questions are quite specific and appear to be quite difficult at first glance. You are seemingly being asked to compare the achievements of every medical mind in history. In reality, you need to pick a topic you are familiar with and develop this. If you are aware that there may be other examples that have had a wider impact then say so before you start your answer. Being aware of your limitation is always a good attribute. What they want you to do is give an example of your wider reading, reflect upon it and share some of your learning. These questions are not all that different from the previous ones. They are simply opportunities to demonstrate self-study skills that are essential for a career in medicine. Self-study is important from the start of undergraduate medicine and continues for evermore as 'life-long learning' and 'continuing professional development'.

Example question and answer from our mentors

Question: *What is the most important discovery in modern medicine?*

Answer: *Well I'm not sure it was the most important or the most modern, but I believe that Joseph Lister's work on antisepsis has had a lasting effect on modern surgery that is just as important today as it was in the 1860s. Between John Snow's work in epidemiology and the spread of disease, and Louis Pasteur and Robert Koch's work on germ theory, doctors were left with a new cause and vector for disease – bacteria and other microorganisms. Lister's major innovation was the use of carbolic acid in operating theatres. This was the first commercially available antiseptic that was safe for human tissue. Before Lister, there was no requirement for surgeons to wash their hands and operating theatres were cleared of 'miasmic disease' by opening the windows. Nowadays every medical student has to learn a 7-stage hand washing technique, before they are allowed to see patients. I had to do the same before my hospital work experience.*

Your turn – write your answer here

Question: *Tell me about an area of medicine or science that interests you*

Answer:

Interview Skills Checklist (inspired by university mark schemes)

Assessment Areas	Very poor	Poor	Below average	Average	Above average	Very good	Excellent	Points
Knowledge of historical medical events								
Knowledge of recent medical advances								
Communicates scientific information clearly and concisely								
Aware of public health, health promotion and education								
Shows evidence of problem solving and comparative analysis								
Overall quality of reflections								

Points total	Percentage Score	Passing score
/42	%	>80% *or* 34/42

Rating	Very poor	Poor	Below average	Average	Above average	Very good	Excellent
Points awarded	1	2	3	4	5	6	7

Interview questions: work experience reflections and insight into a medical career

Typical interview questions that come under this topic

- ✓ Tell me about your work experience.
- ✓ What is the most important thing you learned during your medical work experience?
- ✓ What experience do you have of healthcare in the community?
- ✓ What secondary care experience do you have?
- ✓ What is the difference between primary and secondary care?

Example question and answer from our mentors

Question: *What is the most important thing you learned during your medical work experience?*

Answer: *I did several work experience placements over 3 years including a GP, a stroke ward, a general surgical ward, a hospice and a nursing home. My main aim was to learn more about medicine so that I could make a relatively informed career decision. I feel that I achieved this and so I am here today. I think that spending 2 weeks in a GP was my most insightful placement. It helped me to appreciate the importance of communication skills, extended patient contact and continuity of care. I know that primary care is usually the first port of call for patients and I directly observed how challenging it is to identify patients' concerns, address them appropriately and prescribe treatment all within 10 minutes. I also saw how GPs modulate their communication for different audiences. For example utilising empathy and reassuring language to relate to distressed patients, then swapping to detailed scientific language in secondary care referral letters and phone calls. I know that communication is a fundamental transferrable skill for doctors and I have been developing mine ever since my GP experience. I now have a GCSE level certificate in communication skills and grade 8 in acting. I look forward to developing these skills further as a medical student and beyond.*

What they want to know

Most questions in this section are fairly general. You will be expected to have a reasonable range of experiences, so some questions may be specific to primary, secondary or community care. At the end of the day it is your learning, reflection and identification and development of transferrable skills that they want to know about. If you were not able to get experience in a hospital- don't worry! The interviewers are aware that some areas offer strict age limits for these placements. In this case you should direct them to your best experiences.

What you need to say

If given the chance, pick a small range of experiences to talk about – or at least allude to having 'varied experience', if they want you to focus upon one only. Use a logical reflective model (Gibbs, Borton etc.) to explain what you have observed and learned. Detail specific reflections and comment upon the transferrable skills you identified. Finally you should mention how you have developed these skills and provide evidence. It is always a good idea to refer to skills development as a process; one that you will continue throughout your professional career.

What not to say

Do not list or provide simple narratives without reflections or evidence of transferrable skills.

'Curveballs' and challenging follow-up questions

- ✓ What was the most challenging aspect of your work experience?
- ✓ What negative aspects of medicine did you notice?
- ✓ Have you experienced any aspects of medicine that made you question your career choice?

What they are actually asking

These follow-up questions are designed to make you reflect. Retelling your experiences is relatively easy, as is highlighting basic transferrable skills such as 'communication' and 'team work'. It requires even more skill to put your experiences into a 'realistic' or 'human' context. Medicine is a difficult job and has many common challenges. The interviewers want to know that you have observed and reflected upon some of these. Furthermore, they want to know these issues have not put you off and you recognise the importance of transferrable skills in overcoming them.

Example question and answer from our mentors

Question: *Have you experienced any aspects of medicine that made you question your career choice?*

Answer: *During my stroke placement, I came across many patients who were severely debilitated. It soon became apparent to me that they could not be cured, and that they were probably not in the right place to receive the care that they needed. Their issues were almost entirely social and they were languishing in hospital, waiting for new care packages or nursing home beds. I saw how many of these patients ended up with hospital-acquired infections and suffered as a result of their extended hospital stays. I did question my career choice at this point. After further reflection and experience shadowing in A&E however, I realised that some stroke patients can be effectively treated with clot lysis. For most patients, the key treatments seem to be identification of risk factors and stroke prevention. Following my hospital experience, I spent time with a GP who provided education to patients on lifestyle factors and how to prevent stroke, heart disease and type 2 diabetes. I understand more about holistic care now; how good healthcare is social as well as medical, involves emergency, acute and preventative approaches and above all should have the patients' best interests at its core. This type of care is holistic and patient-centred.*

Your turn – write your answer here

Question: *What was the most challenging aspect of your work experience?*

Answer:

Interview Skills Checklist (inspired by university mark schemes)

Assessment Areas	Very poor	Poor	Below average	Average	Above average	Very good	Excellent	Points
Range of work experiences								
Quality of work experiences								
Identification of learning points								
Transferrable skills identified								
Demonstrates desirable attributes of a doctor								
Overall quality of reflections								

Points total	Percentage Score	Passing score
/42	%	**>80% *or* 34/42**

Rating	Very poor	Poor	Below average	Average	Above average	Very good	Excellent
Points awarded	**1**	**2**	**3**	**4**	**5**	**6**	**7**

Interview questions: transferrable skills and desirable attributes for a future doctor

Typical interview questions that come under this topic

- ✓ What do you understand by the term, 'transferrable skills?'
- ✓ What skills did you observe during your work experience, which are applicable to medicine?
- ✓ What essential skills are required of modern junior doctors?
- ✓ What different skill sets do different doctors require?
- ✓ Can you give me an example of a time you demonstrated team working or leadership skills.
- ✓ Why do doctors need to be excellent communicators?

Example question and answer from our mentors

Question: *What essential skills are required of modern junior doctors?*

Answer: *During my work experience, I observed doctors from many different specialties in their daily working lives. I saw how junior doctors on wards work in teams to distribute jobs and treat patients more efficiently. I recognise the importance of these skills and I have developed my own team-working skills as captain of my school rugby team. It was my responsibility to monitor the individual players' positions and performance in team manoeuvres. I then had to discuss technical 'set pieces of play' with our coach and feedback improvements to the rest of my team, whilst inspiring them to keep giving 100% effort. I saw how GPs modulate their communication, utilising empathy to relate to patients and precise scientific language when making referrals. I gained experience in adapting my communication when I volunteered at a home for learning disabled adults. I had to speak slowly, clearly and with lots of facial expressions and body language. I think these skills will be essential as a junior doctor as many patients have reduced communication abilities for various reasons, including stroke, learning disability and very young children.*

What they want to know

This section overlaps greatly with work experience. If you have already reflected upon transferrable skills in those answers then you may have already covered many of the scoring points for this section. Interviewers may adjust their questions to highlight specific transferrable kills that you have not yet mentioned.

What you need to say

Generally speaking, you need to identify a few specific transferrable skills, give evidence to support where you observed them and explain how you have developed them in yourself. You also need to comment upon their direct application to medicine and how and where they could be utilised. The point you are trying to make is that you will be a better candidate for medicine because you have skills essential for the job and you know exactly how to apply them.

What not to say

Be wary of sounding too proficient at anything. All skills are developed through a process that takes years. You may feel confident now, but you will be faced by many new and challenging experiences as a doctor. You need to emphasise that you plan to develop your skills throughout medical school and beyond, adapting them to a continually changing workplace (and patients).

'Curveballs' and challenging follow-up questions

- ✓ What undesirable attributes do you think make a bad doctor?
- ✓ Do have an example of poor communication in a clinical setting?
- ✓ Tell me about one of your skills that requires further development.
- ✓ Why is team work bad?

What they are actually asking

These questions are often difficult as many of us forget to record or do not like commenting upon negative experiences. This is an important part of reflective practice, which is an essential skill that doctors must possess in order to deliver safe patient care. Observing poor or lacking skills helps you to appreciate the situations where these skills are essential for effective patient care. They are expecting you to describe some negative experiences and detail why they were lacking transferrable skills. Another level of difficulty comes when you are asked about your own limitations. You can actually spin this into something more positive by explaining that you are aware of these weaknesses and that you have taken action to try and improve them. This demonstrates that you are humble, but committed to learning and doing better – all of which are great attributes for medicine.

Example question and answer from our mentors

Question: *Tell me about one of your skills that requires further development.*

Answer: *I have always had difficulty with confidence and presenting my work in front of other people. I recognised that this was an issue when I decided to study medicine and started my work experience in a local hospital. I observed how confidently the junior doctors on the stroke ward spoke to patients and their colleagues. I know confidence is an important part of communication as it helps you to speak clearly and precisely. I have seen how essential this is when junior doctors were relaying clinical information about deteriorating patients to consultants. Following these reflections, I enrolled in an after school acting club. I have now been attending twice a week for a year and I am about to sit my grade 6 in public speaking. I now feel much more confident and I think I have managed to turn one of my biggest weaknesses into one of my greatest assets. Furthermore, I have developed a key skill that will aid me throughout my medical career. I look forward to developing my communication skills further as a medical student.*

Your turn – write your answer here

Question: *Do have an example of poor communication in a clinical setting?*

Answer:

Interview Skills Checklist (inspired by university mark schemes)

Assessment Areas	Very poor	Poor	Below average	Average	Above average	Very good	Excellent	Points
Evidence of teaching and presentation								
Evidence of leadership and team-working								
Identification of skills via work experience								
Demonstrates empathy								
Appreciation of continuing professional development								
Overall quality of reflections								

Points total	Percentage Score	Passing score
/42	%	**>80% *or* 34/42**

Rating	Very poor	Poor	Below average	Average	Above average	Very good	Excellent
Points awarded	**1**	**2**	**3**	**4**	**5**	**6**	**7**

Interview questions: extracurricular activities, well roundedness and stress outlets

Typical interview questions that come under this topic

- ✓ Tell me about your hobbies.
- ✓ What do you do for fun?
- ✓ How will you manage the stress associated with a medical curriculum?
- ✓ Apart from academics, what else have you excelled in?
- ✓ Are you interested in joining any of the medical school sports teams or societies?

Example question and answer from our mentors

Question: *How will you manage the stress associated with a medical curriculum?*

Answer: *I have spoken to lots of medical students and I know the workload is large. Currently I spend a lot of my free time playing sports and going to drama club. I find these to be great opportunities to deal with the stress of my A-levels and meet up with my friends. The have added benefits too – rugby keeps me fit and gives me more energy to study; drama has really helped to develop my communication and interpersonal skills. My extracurricular activities are really important to me and help me to lead a balanced life. I am really keen to continue rugby and drama at medical school and I asked specifically about these activities at the open day. It turns out that the university has a dedicated medics' dramatic society, and a medics' rugby team. I look forward to representing my medical school in one of these and perhaps to try something new.*

What they want to know

Basically they want to know that you have interests outside of academic work and studying. This is mainly to do with stress outlets, being a balanced human being and having the potential to enjoy yourself at medical school. It is no secret that if you are happy and enjoy what you are doing; you will do better and be more successful.

What you need to say

Be specific about a few extracurricular activities and comment upon the social and indirect academic benefits. In other words, these activities help you to spend time with friends and de-stress. Words such as, 'sustainability' and 'balance' help to clarify these points. Try to make links to the specific institution as well. This is a good opportunity to demonstrate that you have done some further research into the medical schools you have applied to. Universities love to hear that you can make them look good. Representing them in extracurricular pursuits is a great way to achieve this - so mention it at the interview!

What not to say

Don't be tempted to list too many activities or to make yourself sound over accomplished, as you may be missing the point of the question. It is not, 'how good are you?' but rather, 'what evidence you can provide to suggest that you will make a sustainable addition to your chosen medical school?' Also remember to reflect on all of your achievements, commenting upon specific learning and how this can be applied to medical school and your future career.

'Curveballs' and challenging follow-up questions

- ✓ What makes you think that you will have time for all of your extracurricular activities at medical school?
- ✓ A few successful candidates drop out of medicine in the first year; why won't you be one of them?
- ✓ You've mention lots of outstanding achievements, but what is your biggest flaw?

What they are actually asking

This is a part of the interview where you are asked to comment upon your achievements and your good points. A common tactic is to turn your answer on its head and get you to focus on an area that isn't so good. This is similar to the 'curveballs' in the 'transferrable skills' section previously, but with good reason. You should expect and plan for some negative questioning, as they are common interview techniques. Remember that medical schools do not want students who already think they know everything. They are looking for students whom they can teach. They want students who know their limitations and who understand the importance of reflective practice and continuing professional development. Therefore, if it all sounds too good, they may want to test you with a negative question. Keep your cool, use a logical model to answer the question (Borton, Gibbs etc) and argue your point methodically. Don't forget that negative questions can be turned into positive answers. Think of your flaws as an 'awareness of your limitations'.

Example question and answer from our mentors

Question: *What is your biggest flaw?*

Answer: *From my work experience shadowing junior doctors on a gastroenterology ward, I learned the importance of accepting one's limitations. In a medical context this helps you to identify situations where you need senior input in order to treat patients safely and effectively. I saw how doctors communicated effectively with their colleagues to prioritise and organise ward tasks such as CT scans and blood tests. Observing these doctors encouraged me to reflect on my own abilities and I concluded that my prioritising and organisational skills were not good. I relied a lot on my parents to plan extracurricular activities for me, and my school to remind me about coursework and exams. I decided to become more organised; I bought a diary and planned a full revision and coursework schedule for the year. I downloaded an app and used it to calculate a weekly budget from my allowance and Saturday job earnings. I took my new organisational skills and applied them to organising a comprehensive portfolio of my work experience including primary, secondary and community care. Being organised helps me to prioritise important tasks and relieves stress. I think these skills will be essential for self-directed study on the PBL course, and for dealing with sick patients as a junior doctor.*

Your turn – write your answer here

Question: *Apart from academics, what else have you excelled in?*

Answer:

Interview Skills Checklist (inspired by university mark schemes)

Assessment Areas	Very poor	Poor	Below average	Average	Above average	Very good	Excellent	Points
Evidence of academic extracurricular pursuits								
Evidence of non-academic extra curricular pursuits								
Ability to organise and prioritise								
Demonstrates potential to contribute to the university								
Ability to cope well with stressful situations								
Evidence of academic extracurricular pursuits								

Points total	Percentage Score	Passing score
/42	**%**	**>80% *or* 34/42**

Rating	Very poor	Poor	Below average	Average	Above average	Very good	Excellent
Points awarded	**1**	**2**	**3**	**4**	**5**	**6**	**7**

Interview questions: socio-cultural awareness, community involvement, caring and charity

Typical interview questions that come under this topic

- ✓ Have you had any experience of community involvement?
- ✓ Tell me about your experiences with different cultures?
- ✓ What are health inequalities; can you give any examples?
- ✓ What contribution do charities make to healthcare in this country?

Example question and answer from our mentors

Question: *What contribution do charities make to healthcare in this country?*

Answer: *During my work experience I spent time working in a Barnardo's charity shop. I also raised money for Cancer Research UK with a cake stall and a charity cross county run. I know that charities play a big role in medicine and society as a whole. Barnardo's for example is the UK's leading children's charity and provides essential services for at risk children including counselling and discussion groups. Cancer Research UK on the other hand, funds high-level scientific research to improve the identification and treatment of cancer. Charities are crucial as they fund many services that cannot be funded by the NHS and would otherwise not exist. I know that this Medical School has many facilities for students to get involved with fundraising and I am very much looking forward to this as an extracurricular activity and an opportunity to meet new people.*

What they want to know

Healthcare is not just about medicine and surgery; it is about people. Selectors want to know that you have gone well beyond your academic work and have done more than just shadow doctors and healthcare professionals. It is important that you demonstrate and appreciate the wider impact of healthcare and the human cost of disease and disability. One way to do this and to exact some positive social change is to get involved with charities. Here you learn more about patient experiences and develop skills such as empathy. Working for charities is also very suggestive of you being a caring and compassionate individual – an area that is important but often overlooked when applying to medical school.

What you need to say

If you have experiences with specific charities then don't forget to mention them. You should expect to be questioned on the charities' roles and actions, so be prepared by doing some research. You can link charity work to transferrable skills and how you might contribute to the medical school or university. Charity work is a great example of extracurricular pursuits that you can also use to demonstrate yourself as a 'balanced individual'.

What not to say

Do not try to claim too much credit for yourself or to embellish your activities. Even if you only raised a small amount for the charity, that had relatively little social impact, you still experienced something and will have gained valuable learning and reflections.

'Curveballs' and challenging follow-up questions

- ✓ What potential problems may cultural minorities face when accessing healthcare services?
- ✓ How do healthcare providers attempt to improve access to healthcare for the elderly?
- ✓ How is multiculturalism influencing public health in this country?

What they are actually asking

These questions are designed to delve deeper into your wider knowledge of UK healthcare. They test your background reading as well as your awareness of current social and political issues. Sometimes the questions might be specific to certain demographic groups such as elderly patients or those from ethnic minorities. Other questions may be broader and you might be able to use specific examples from your own experience. If ever you do not know an answer to a question then say so because they might give you another question from the same topic that is easier to answer. In most situations however, you should be able to think around the problem.

Example question and answer from our mentors

Question: *What potential problems may ethnic minority patients face when accessing healthcare?*

Answer: *On my shadowing experience in A&E I saw many patients from different ethnic and cultural backgrounds. Some of them spoke English but others didn't and therefore had significant language barriers. I was impressed by how junior doctors adapted their communication for these patients, but in some cases it was necessary to use a phone translation service. A&E is an intimidating environment at the best of times, with doctors and nurses rushing around. It must be much more confusing if you cannot understand what is going on. In addition to language, many ethnic minorities, foreign nationals and non-UK residents are not registered with a GP and are therefore forced to come to A&E. It is encouraging to see that there are some foreign language facilities in A&E. On reflection, I think community health education outreach programmes could be effective in redirecting some patients to primary care, a local pharmacy or other non-emergency services. I look forward to learning more about health promotion and public health during my time at medical school.*

Your turn – write you answer here

Question: *How is multiculturalism influencing public health in this country?*

Answer:

Interview Skills Checklist (inspired by university mark schemes)

Assessment Areas	Very poor	Poor	Below average	Average	Above average	Very good	Excellent	Points
Evidence of community involvement								
Awareness of socio-cultural issues in medicine								
Awareness of health inequalities and barriers to healthcare								
Evidence of caring and compassion								
Is courteous and respectful								
Overall quality of reflections								

Points total	Percentage Score	Passing score
/42	**%**	**>80% *or* 34/42**

Rating	Very poor	Poor	Below average	Average	Above average	Very good	Excellent
Points awarded	**1**	**2**	**3**	**4**	**5**	**6**	**7**

Interview questions: knowledge of modern NHS structure and practice

Typical interview questions that come under this topic

- ✓ What do you know about the Health and Social Care Act?
- ✓ What do you know about the BMA, NICE and the GMC?
- ✓ What GMC publications are you aware of?
- ✓ What are evidence-based medicine and patient-centred care?

Example question and answer from our mentors

Question: What do you know about the BMA, NICE and the GMC and what they do?

Answer: On my work experience, I had the chance to speak to several different doctors about their careers. I was directed to the general medical council or GMC. From my own reading, I know that they are the regulatory body for doctors and they are responsible for monitoring training and professional standards. They produce documents and guidance to help doctors remain professional and engage in high quality practice. Most relevant to me is 'Tomorrow's Doctors', which sets out clear learning outcomes for medical students and attributes required of newly qualified doctors. The British Medical Association on the other hand, is a trade union. It supports doctors in their working lives via union support, and discussions with trusts or the government about pay and working conditions. The National Institute for Health and Clinical Excellence or NICE, is an independent body whose job it is to review medications, and the treatment of diseases. They produce evidence-based guidelines for doctors so that they can practise safe, patient-centred care.

What they want to know

This section is quite knowledge heavy. Generally speaking, the interviewers are looking for clear evidence of wider reading but also an understanding of some fundamental concepts in healthcare. For example evidence-based medicine, patient-centred care and often some basic ethico-legal concepts too. You often get multiple questions in this section to probe your understanding of concepts, and to check that you are not just repeating buzzwords. The answer above would logically lead to further questioning about 'evidence-based medicine' and 'patient-centred care'.

What you need to say

If they give you acronyms then make it clear you know what they stand for. If they give you concepts then define them. You may also be asked to give examples of where you have seen these concepts being applied. Refer back to your work experience or mention some current issues in the media.

What not to say

Do not guess in this section, you either know or you do not know the answer to some of these questions. You could however say that you are not sure but then make an educated guess using reason and logic. For example if you do not know a textbook definition for 'evidence-based medicine', you could work your way around it and then give a few work experience examples. The point is that all is not lost and acknowledging your limitations is good practice; even better would be to read up on these topics before the interview.

'Curveballs' and challenging follow-up questions

- ✓ Can you tell me about Public Health England?
- ✓ What do you know about privatisation of the NHS?
- ✓ What are CCGs and what is their purpose?

What they are actually asking

Curveballs for this section are really just more difficult questions or topics. If you answer well, you may be asked to speak about another topic. As with most knowledge-based answers, if you have read up on them they shouldn't be difficult. You will need to provide appropriate examples to get all of the marks. There is a useful chapter about important organisations and their respective roles in the MASTERCLASS guide.

Example question and answer from our mentors

Question: *What are CCGs and what are they for?*

Answer: *Clinical Commissioning Groups were introduced in the Health and Social Care Act (2012) and partially replaced primary care trusts (PCTs). They are groups of healthcare professionals from primary and secondary care, and also non-medical managers. Currently, they are responsible for distributing funds that are provided by NHS England. This money used to go to PCTs but is now available for the 'commissioning' of community, elective and emergency patient care.*

Your turn – write your answer here

Question: *What is patient-centred care?*

Answer:

Interview Skills Checklist (inspired by university mark schemes)

Assessment Areas	Very poor	Poor	Below average	Average	Above average	Very good	Excellent	Points
Understands difference between primary, secondary and community care								
Basic knowledge of NHS funding structure								
Awareness of medical organisations								
Ability to communicate effectively and concisely								
Evidence of wider reading								
Overall quality of reflections								

Points total	Percentage Score	Passing score
/42	**%**	**>80% *or* 34/42**

Rating	Very poor	Poor	Below average	Average	Above average	Very good	Excellent
Points awarded	**1**	**2**	**3**	**4**	**5**	**6**	**7**

Interview questions: awareness of topical NHS and international health issues

Typical interview questions that come under this topic:

- ✓ What effect does an aging UK population have on healthcare?
- ✓ How does lifestyle factors such as alcohol, smoking and unhealthy eating affect healthcare?
- ✓ Tell me about some topical issues that are currently affecting the NHS.
- ✓ What major international health issues are you aware of, and how do they affect the UK?

Example question and answer from our mentors

Question: *What effect does an aging UK population have on healthcare?*

Answer: *During my hospital experience I spent time on geriatric and general medical wards. I noticed how many of the older patients spent longer in hospital and I discussed this issue with some of the doctors. I learned how elderly people tend to have more co-morbidities including heart disease, lung disease and joint problems. This is not always due to age exactly; health education was not as good in previous generations and smoking was considered to be socially acceptable. I also learned about social care and the need to reintroduce patients back into their communities, safely. Many elderly patients have mobility problems or minimal support at home. These individuals often have extended hospital stays as the risk of sending them home is too high – they might fall, become unwell again or otherwise end up back in hospital. In summary, we are facing an aging population. Currently many elderly patients require more time in hospital but with recent advances in public health, this picture may change. In a generation's time when I am a senior doctor, older patients may be healthier and the bigger problems may come from obesity and diabetes in young to middle-aged patients.*

What they want to know

Let them know that you are aware of current health issues relating to the above topics. They also want to see that you have had first hand experience with some of these types of patients, so don't forget to refer to your work experience. If you can refer to current news stories or journal articles this will show good insight.

What you need to say

Ideally you should give specific examples, reflect on them and clearly state your learning. You should also detail further reading and other sources including healthcare professionals. Make sure you answer their questions directly but if you can refer to other topical issues as well, it will suggest that you posses comprehensive background knowledge.

What not to say

Try not to be accusatory in this section – do not blame elderly or obese patients, or otherwise appear to be making value judgements. Take a general approach and comment upon contributing factors, such as poor health education in previous generations.

'Curveballs' and challenging follow-up questions

- ✓ Why are A&E services in the UK facing an increasing workload?
- ✓ What factors are contributing to the rising costs of healthcare in the United Kingdom?
- ✓ What is the future of medicine?
- ✓ What is the biggest threat to UK healthcare?

What they are actually asking

These questions are also testing your knowledge of topical healthcare issues. They are more difficult for a number of reasons. Some are specific to 'costs' or a particular healthcare service (A&E). One question is broad but asks you to speculate on the future and the other question asks you to place a negative value judgement upon the UK population. The point of these questions is to stimulate you to think as well as regurgitate facts. The idea is to take what you know and what you have learned from your experiences, and apply this knowledge to a new concept. This type of 'forward thinking' and logical deduction is highly desirable in medical students. After all, you are the future of medicine and you may well be involved in the management or commissioning of future healthcare.

Example question and answer from our mentors

Question: *Why are A&E services in the UK facing an increasing workload?*

Answer: *I managed to arrange a week's work experience in a busy A&E department. I observed several cases and spent time talking to nurses, doctors and the patient flow team. I was surprised to learn that in a recent audit, only half of the cases in a particular month were considered to be true emergencies. The general consensus in A&E seemed to be that most non-emergency patients turn up as they cannot or do not have appropriate access to a GP. I know that some non-UK residents are here for a short time and do not register with a GP. I also learned from my GP placement that many UK patients have to wait weeks for an appointment with their doctor. According to the GPs I spoke to, this is the result of a national shortage of doctors being recruited to general practice. It seems that the government has taken notice of this and they are implementing a new recruitment drive to combat the issue. At present, patients are faced with a long wait to see a GP, or instant access to a free walk-in service that may actually get them to a specialist quicker. Out-of-hours GP services do exist but are currently not making a big impact. Hence the government is pushing for a 7-day GP service. Only time will tell if this service materialises and whether it will work.*

Your turn – write your answer here

Question: How do lifestyle factors such as alcohol, smoking and unhealthy eating affect healthcare?

Answer:

Interview Skills Checklist (inspired by university mark schemes)

Assessment Areas	Very poor	Poor	Below average	Average	Above average	Very good	Excellent	Points
Awareness of UK demographic factors affecting the NHS								
Awareness of lifestyle factors affecting the NHS								
Awareness of political factors affecting the NHS								
Awareness of financial factors affecting the NHS								
Appreciation of current and future NHS developments								
Overall quality of reflections								

Points total	Percentage Score	Passing score
/42	**%**	**>80% *or* 34/42**

Rating	Very poor	Poor	Below average	Average	Above average	Very good	Excellent
Points awarded	**1**	**2**	**3**	**4**	**5**	**6**	**7**

Interview questions: knowledge and understanding of basic medical ethics and law

Typical interview questions that come under this topic

- ✓ **Scenario:** You observe a junior doctor shouting at a nurse. What would you do?
- ✓ **Scenario:** A junior colleague tells you that she saw another junior doctor taking drugs at a music event. What are the main issues involved and how would you address each of them?
- ✓ **Scenario:** Your junior colleague is frequently late to work, leaving you to do most of the jobs. How would you address this situation?

Example question and answer from our mentors

Scenario: *Your junior doctor colleague is frequently late to work, leaving you to do most of the jobs. How would you address this situation?*

Response: *I'm dealing with quite a few 'unknowns' here so I would like to clarify a few things. I would first like to broach the issue with my colleague in a confidential place to check whether they are OK.*

Question: *It turns out your colleague's father has passed and they have not been coping. What would you do?*

Response: *I know that I have a duty of care to my trust, colleagues and patients. I would suggest that they speak to their educational supervisor as soon as possible. If they agree, I would do my best to support them at work by helping out with their jobs and daily tasks.*

Question: *It has been 3 weeks, your colleague's performance has not improved and your work is now suffering. What would you do?*

Response: *I would explain to my colleague that unless they are willing to see their supervisor I would have to raise concerns. I would do my colleague the courtesy of letting them know my plans, then offering them the chance to act.*

Question: *Would you ever consider talking to anybody else about this issue?*

Response: *I would aim to involve as few people as possible to prevent harm to my colleague. If their educational supervisor was not available then I could ask my own or inform my colleague's clinical supervisor. These senior doctors are best placed to deal with the issues and informing any of them would be an appropriate escalation of the issue, in keeping with my professional duty.*

Question: *What if your colleague started acting inappropriately or dangerously in the clinical area?*

Response: *There is now an immediate threat to patient safety and this supersedes my duty of care to my colleague. I would immediately escalate this issue to the most senior doctor on the ward, preferably a clinical supervisor. This would actually still be in my colleagues best interests, if their actions are a product of 'not coping' with recent events. If my colleague were acting so inappropriately that they posed a physical risk to patients and staff then I would call security or the police. If they were still reasonable, I might consider encouraging them to leave the 'patient zone' and then consult a supervisor. In any situation, I would have to take on the duties left by my colleague to ensure patient safety. If there were other junior doctors available I would work as a team with them to share the workload.*

What they want to know

Ethical scenarios like this normally consist of several parts: the initial scenario then a series of additional questions or information statements. This usually leads to an escalation in the situation and requires further action. You need to state exactly what you would do at each stage and justify your answers using some basic ethical, professional or legal concepts. Here is a list of major concepts that you should know about:

- ✓ Ethical fundamental principles: *autonomy, beneficence (best interests), non-maleficence (harm prevention) and justice (the law),*
- ✓ *Confidentiality,*

- ✓ *Futility,*
- ✓ *Patient safety,*
- ✓ *Competence and capacity to make decisions,*
- ✓ *Enduring or lasting power of attorney,*
- ✓ *Advanced directives and statements,*
- ✓ *Fairness and truthfulness,*
- ✓ *Honesty and integrity,*
- ✓ *Euthanasia, abortion and assisted dying.*

What you need to say

Answer all questions directly, stating your actions and justifications. It also helps to mention what you would not do and why, as these may be logical follow-up questions. You can suggest multiple options that are equally valid and this makes your logic appear more comprehensive. Normally you will find that the interviewers provide you with additional information at this point, such as certain professionals not being available to contact. This is their way of encouraging you to pick a course of action as you do get marks for decision-making.

What not to say

Do not make unjustified value statements. It is also essential that you pick a standpoint or option. Not making a decision or saying you 'don't know what to do' is not really an option here. This is because most of the marks are for your thought process and the logical deduction that you demonstrate. These scenarios are tricky because there are rarely clear or categorically correct responses. Instead, there is a range of responses that are acceptable depending upon how you justify your actions – with reference to the key concepts above. Refer back to the first chapter of this book for more guidance on ethical scenario questions. There is also an entire chapter about ethical principles in the MASTERCLASS guide.

Here are some more ethical scenarios for you to practise with

- ✓ **Scenario:** You notice a senior doctor acting strangely in the clinical area. What would you do?
- ✓ **Scenario:** A senior colleague comes to work smelling of alcohol. What would you do?
- ✓ **Scenario:** A patient asks you to help them end their life. What is your response to this?
- ✓ **Scenario:** What would you do if you administered the wrong medication to a patient?

In the medical interview, these questions are likely to be semi-structured. Interviewers normally have a list of potential questions or topics that relate to your responses to each situation. Some interviewers take a more free-form approach and respond differently to each candidate depending upon which route their responses take. For this reason it is difficult to craft a specific model question. Instead we have given you a list of scenarios. From this we have taken one scenario and given you a list of likely questions that might arise in an interview. Try responding to each question as in the worked example, or better still, anticipate the question and factor your responses into a well-crafted comprehensive answer, laying out a clear and coherent argument. Bear in mind that ethical questions are designed to test your logical deduction. If interviewers become aware that you may be applying a prepared answer from a similar practice scenario, they may well turn the tables on you and introduce additional factors such as 'aggressive staff members' or 'delirious patients' with 'fluctuating capacity', to simulate your reasoning and ability to adapt to changing situations. On this point, make sure that you explain all of your thought processes out loud. Even if the interviewers are not totally sold on your responses and proposed actions, you can still get marks for your working – a bit like a CGSE maths examination.

Your turn – write your answer here

Scenario: *You observe a junior doctor shouting at a nurse – what would you do?*

Question: *Who would you inform about the doctor's behaviour?*

Question: *Would you approach the doctor yourself? What would you say or do?*

Question: *Would you approach the nurse yourself? What would you say or do?*

Question: *What are the fundamental ethical and professional issues raised by this scenario?*

Question: *How is this issue likely to be resolved and what are the potential consequences?*

Response:

Interview Skills Checklist (inspired by university mark schemes)

Assessment Areas	Very poor	Poor	Below average	Average	Above average	Very good	Excellent	Points
Understanding of fundamental medical ethical principles								
Awareness of basic ethico-legal concepts (e.g. capacity and competence)								
Awareness of basic professional duties (e.g. patient safety and confidentiality)								
Follows a process of logical deduction								
Forms a coherent and well justified argument								
Overall quality of reflections								

Points total	Percentage Score	Passing score
/42	**%**	**>80% *or* 34/42**

Rating	Very poor	Poor	Below average	Average	Above average	Very good	Excellent
Points awarded	**1**	**2**	**3**	**4**	**5**	**6**	**7**

Interview questions: questions aimed more at graduate students

Typical interview questions that come under this topic

- ✓ How has your undergraduate degree prepared you to study medicine?
- ✓ The 4-year graduate entry course in our school is very intensive. How can you demonstrate that you will be able to deal with this increased level of stress?
- ✓ What evidence do you have of scientific research ability from your previous studies?
- ✓ Tell me about your dissertation project and how it relates to medicine.

Example question and answer from our mentors

Question: The 4-year graduate entry course in our school is very intensive. How can you demonstrate that you will be able to deal with this increased level of stress?

Answer: *I did a BSc in Clinical Sciences. I studied core medical sciences including cell biology, histopathology and systems-based anatomy. My course structure was specifically designed to put medical sciences into a clinical context, and it did this by integrating scientific theory with clinical case discussions and interactive seminars. I have researched the curriculum at your medical school and I feel that I am already familiar with much of the pre-clinical content. I know that the early part of the course is intense but I feel prepared specifically for this type of study. Furthermore, I have demonstrated my academic ability by achieving a first in my honours degree. I plan to continue my commitment by studying hard, throughout my medical degree and beyond. In fact I have already made enquiries about the intercalated MSc in Clinical Biology that you have available. It is my intention to pursue an academic foundation post and I think the MSc will make me a highly competitive applicant.*

What they want to know

Medical Schools need to know that you have the academic ability to deal with the intensity of their curricula. For undergraduates they would test this with a standardised set of grades such as A-levels or the International Baccalaureate. Undergraduate degrees on the other hand are more variable – both in subject and institution. Essentially, selectors are looking for a degree in a subject that is highly relevant to medicine, and in which you have scored highly – an upper second-class classification or above. It shouldn't really matter where you have studied. Be aware that as demand is high for graduate places, medical schools frequently ask for B's or above at A-level (or an equivalent secondary-level qualification).

What you need to say

Detail your qualification and classification, and specify what features make it relevant and applicable to undergraduate medical study. It is a good idea to mention any further academic plans that you have, or any other ways in which you could contribute to the institution. Generally speaking only your first undergraduate degree is counted, unless stated otherwise.

What not to say

Do not presume that where you studied will have much impact upon the selectors. It is the relevance of your degree to medicine and the classification you achieved that counts. Try not to talk down other undergraduate degrees or institutions.

'Curveballs' and challenging follow-up questions

- ✓ What do you know about widening access to medical school?
- ✓ What do you know about academic medicine?

What they are actually asking

Some universities have special relationships with internal or external courses that are closely allied to medicine. Some of these may be stand-alone degrees whereas others may be defined as 'access courses' with atypical routes into medicine. If you have studied on one of these courses it is likely to be part of a 'widening access' or 'widening participation' programme. You should therefore be familiar with these concepts before you reach the interview. Another advantage of having done previous post-secondary study is the development of research skills. During an undergraduate degree you will have developed essay writing and scientific research skills. You may be asked directly about these at interview and whether you want to continue with academic study during your degree. Some postgraduate medical students intercalate in a Masters degree or even a PhD (to achieve a combined MBPhD qualification). If you are considering academic medicine as an option then do mention it at interview. It demonstrates career insight, enthusiasm and makes you sound like a good investment to a medical school selector.

Example question and answer from our mentors

Question: *What do you know about academic medicine?*

Answer: *I have always been interested in research and my undergraduate degree in medical sciences has provided me with essential essay writing and scientific research techniques. I am keen to develop my interest in medical sciences via an intercalated MSc. I am aware that this Medical School offers several interesting options. My plan after this would be to pursue a career in academic medicine via academic foundation programme, clinical fellowship and clinical lectureship routes. From my reading I have learned that it is possible to become a clinician scientist at consultant level with your work split evenly between research and clinical practice. I feel that this career option would suit my personality and make the most of my skills. Ultimately, I would like to become a professor but firstly I would like to spend time during my medical degree, exploring research topics through student selected components and an elective project. I currently have an interest in cardiovascular biology and synthetic heart valves, but I look forward to discovering new topics next year.*

Your turn – write your answer here

Question: *How has your undergraduate degree prepared you to study medicine?*

Answer:

Interview Skills Checklist (inspired by university mark schemes)

Assessment Areas	Very poor	Poor	Below average	Average	Above average	Very good	Excellent	Points
Motivation for medicine								
Quality and applicability of undergraduate study								
Additional academic achievements								
Additional extracurricular achievement								
Potential for contribution to the institution								
Overall quality of reflections								

Points total	Percentage Score	Passing score
/42	%	>80% *or* 34/42

Rating	Very poor	Poor	Below average	Average	Above average	Very good	Excellent
Points awarded	1	2	3	4	5	6	7

Interview questions: questions more specific to Oxbridge students

Typical interview questions that come under this topic

- ✓ In your statement you mentioned PET and CT scanners – what are those and how do they work?
- ✓ Why is HIV so bad?
- ✓ What do you know about the pathophysiology of cancer?
- ✓ How does your body fight disease?

Example question and answer from our mentors

Question: *Why is HIV so bad?*

Answer: *HIV is a degenerative and (currently) incurable chronic disease. It is devastating to patients as it leads to multiple diseases and early death. Objectively it can be assessed in terms of morbidity and mortality, pathophysiology and public health impact. Human Immunodeficiency Virus is an autoimmune retrovirus that attacks CD4+ and other leucocytes. It gradually depletes these cells, which are key factors in the body's cell-mediated immune system. When the CD4+ count is very low, the patient has developed acquired immunodeficiency Syndrome (AIDS). At this point, HIV patients are highly immuno-compromised and are susceptible to opportunistic infections such as pneumocystis pneumonia, and other diseases such as Kaposi's sarcoma. The most dangerous feature from a transmission perspective is the lack of initial symptoms of infection. It can be passed in most body fluid and is prevalent amongst intravenous drug users (IVDUs). It is difficult to combat, as it is normally symptoms that prompt patients to seek help. IVDUs are also using illegal substances and may be afraid of exposing their activities. Finally HIV has a significant stigma attached to it and this may prevent some individuals from getting tested. In summary, HIV is a degenerative, incurable chronic disease. It leads to significant morbidity and premature death. Its symptoms are often absent and it is easily transferrable through body fluids. There are also social barriers that prevent patients from seeking help. Ironically, there are now highly effective treatments to delay the onset of AIDS and many patients can live a full and happy life for decades after diagnosis.*

What they want to know

Oxbridge schools tend to have multiple traditional style interviews. They like to focus upon detailed scientific questions then logical deduction questions that make you think outside the box. You may find some questions where you are given graphs or images and asked to apply your knowledge to understand them. Alternatively you may have to use a mixture of your science knowledge and abstract thinking to give the best answer. You should expect to be tested to the limit of your awareness. Just because you have run out of things to stay, does not mean you have given them insufficient information. They may be pushing you to get a better idea of the extent of your comprehension. The key is to stay calm and continue to think logically by using common sense and what you already know.

What you need to say

When faced with detailed scientific questions, you need to state everything you know in a logical manner. Try splitting it into sections such as, 'pathophysiology', 'public health issues', or 'social impact'. This also helps you to organise your points. Sometimes these questions are specific to a certain disease (like HIV above) or you will be invited to speak about broader topics. If you do get more freedom then choose a topic you know well from several perspectives. You should also expect to be questioned on fine details and you may be asked to advocate the opposing point of view. For example in the question above it could be turned on its head to ask, 'why is HIV not as bad as other diseases such as diabetes and cancer?' This not only tests your knowledge of several scientific topics, but also brings in your ability to utilise logic and reason to compare similarly destructive chronic diseases. To get full points you would need to choose the 'lesser of these evils' and clearly justify your standpoint.

What not to say

Do not state the obvious or make unjustified comments without reference to scientific theory or your wider reading. You can assume that the interviewers are familiar with the topics they ask about but don't forget to mention all reasoning and thought processes out loud. These may stimulate further questioning from the interviewers or they may decide to guide you back on track if you have veered off course. These types of questions are clearly difficult, however the interview is an information gathering process, and it is still the interviewers job to extract as much information from you as they need, to tick the boxes on their checklists. Try not to panic and automatically assume that you cannot answer the question, just because you were not expecting it. It is perfectly reasonable to take a moment to think through the problem before you start your answer.

'Curveballs' and challenging follow-up questions

- ✓ Define death
- ✓ How would you fix the NHS?
- ✓ What is the most successful organism on earth?
- ✓ Why are seeded grapes better than seedless ones?
- ✓ Why do cats' eyes glow in the dark?

What they are actually asking

Curveballs for Oxbridge-style questions are usually the more obscure or broad and undefined questions. They are usually questions that have multiple and complex answers, and are designed to see how you negotiate uncertainty, utilise clear logic and ultimately arrive at a justifiable conclusion. For these reasons, you need to be very clear about how you decide upon your answers. Occasionally you can ask for more information but it is normally left to you to define the parameters of the question. As a rule of thumb, you will need to go beyond generic knowledge in your science curriculum. You may also have to refer to other allied subjects such as maths and geography. If the question is very topical then you will be expected to demonstrate your wider medical reading, knowledge of NHS issues and current affairs that affect healthcare. Essentially, the more complete and well rounded your answer; the more credit you should receive. If you have missed any key areas you may be questioned further on these and still be able to get the marks.

Example question and answer from our mentors

Question: *What is the most successful organism on earth?*

Answer: *If you measure success by intelligence, complexity and power, then humans are archetypal organisms. We have conquered land, sea and air and harnessed the power of technology. That said, our success is as nothing if measured in pure numbers, adaptation ability and reproductive advantage. We are an aging population with diminishing reproduction and an increasing susceptibility to pandemic diseases. For true success in this arena we have to look at microorganisms, in particular bacteria. They are the most numerous of all organisms; they exist in virtually all environments from toxic waste to acidic hot springs. Bacteria regularly adapt to antibiotics that have been specifically engineered to destroy them. Scientists are now hailing this as the age of bacteria. You could even argue that bacteria have power over humans, as we cannot live without some commensal gut bacteria. Viruses are perhaps as prolific as bacteria, but they are not truly living organisms.*

Your turn – write your answer here

Question: How does your body fight disease?

Answer:

Interview Skills Checklist (inspired by university mark schemes)

Assessment Areas	Very poor	Poor	Below average	Average	Above average	Very good	Excellent	Points
Evidence of extracurricular academic excellence								
Ability to think laterally and employ logic and reason to unfamiliar situations								
Appreciation of wider issues affecting healthcare								
Ability to construct a coherent and well justified argument								
Ability to think under pressure and remain calm								
Overall quality of reflections								

Points total	Percentage Score	Passing score
/42	**%**	**>80% *or* 34/42**

Rating	Very poor	Poor	Below average	Average	Above average	Very good	Excellent
Points awarded	**1**	**2**	**3**	**4**	**5**	**6**	**7**

Part 3b: Interview skills checklists: **MMI Stations**

Medic Mentor's Part 2 Mock Interview Skills Course runs in London each year. Registration is £45 and includes personalised feedback and mark schemes. Visit www.medicmentor.org to register and find courses near you.

- ✓ Attend a 'real-life' mock medical school interview.
- ✓ You will be interviewed by a range of medical doctors and students.
- ✓ Interview questions are similar to those asked at medical school interviews.
- ✓ Get the chance to undertake a panel-interview and an MMI.
- ✓ Get personalised individual feedback on your performance.
- ✓ Attend 'Interview Skills' small-group workshops.
- ✓ Proceeds are donated to a UK registered charity.

MMI stations: written communication – no invigilator, written answers

Typical MMI stations that come under this topic

- ✓ Who was the most influential person in modern medicine?
- ✓ What is the biggest issue currently facing the NHS?
- ✓ What is the next big development in hospital medicine?
- ✓ Which single healthcare intervention has had the biggest effect upon UK population health?

Top tips from our mentors

Anything is fair game in this type of station. You will find however that the topics are all fairly broad, so that you have plenty to write about. Medical schools appreciate that many students have limited experience of essay writing, and you only have 5-10 minutes to make your points and justify them. With this in mind, keep things concise, succinct and try to avoid waffle. Occasionally, they may appear overly specific to an area you have not studied – like public health. Generally you can apply a bit of common sense and work out most of the fundamental issues they want you to explore.

What they want to know

Medical schools want to know that you have put your career choice into context. They want you to have an appreciation for medical history and how it has led to changes in practice; to have knowledge of more recent medical and surgical advances and their impact; and to have an awareness of future developments that are likely to change the way you will practice medicine. These questions are designed to draw out your 'wider insight into medicine'. You need to demonstrate depth and breadth of knowledge and understanding of real world applications. You must also sound enthusiastic! All of this suggests you will do well in a career that is scientific, social and ever more political.

What you need to write, do or say

You should always aim to answer questions directly. Choose appropriate options and justify your answers with specific examples. Many of these questions seem unrealistic or subjective. This is because they want you to deliver your opinion (albeit well reasoned and appropriately justified). In a sense it doesn't matter what the answer is to a specific question. The likelihood is that it is a controversial issue open to interpretation anyway. Your job is to pick a standpoint and some reasonable examples. Compare your position with other options and describe why you feel they are not as appropriate. You should also aim to criticise your own position and point out the features that prevent it from being perfect. You should then summarise and say why, on balance, you have chosen the best option. This logical approach makes you appear open-minded. Including lots of examples makes you appear well read.

Try not to range too widely in your answers; it wastes times and you are less likely to be providing high quality examples. You should use a logical model to reflect upon the points you make and examples you use e.g. Borton, Gibbs, STARR etc.

Your turn – write your answer here

Question: *What is the next big development in hospital medicine?*

Answer:

Interview Skills Checklist (inspired by university mark schemes)

Assessment Areas	Very poor	Poor	Below average	Average	Above average	Very good	Excellent	Points
Answer questions directly								
Draws upon specific examples for justification								
Provides a balanced argument								
Summarises points and draws conclusions								
Forms a coherent argument, utilising logic and reason								
Overall quality of reflections								

Points total	Percentage Score	Passing score
/42	%	**>80% *or* 34/42**

Rating	Very poor	Poor	Below average	Average	Above average	Very good	Excellent
Points awarded	**1**	**2**	**3**	**4**	**5**	**6**	**7**

MMI stations: verbal communication, role-play and empathising

Typical MMI stations that come under this topic

- ✓ An 11-year-old female patient has come to your GP surgery for her HPV vaccine. She is accompanied by her mother and does not want to have the procedure done. Explore her concerns.
- ✓ A 60-year-old woman has been waiting in A&E for three hours. She asks to speak to a doctor, as she wants to know what is happening. She is third in line to be seen by a doctor. Explore her concerns.
- ✓ A 19-year-old male is unconscious but stable in A&E after a road traffic accident. His father arrives, very distressed, and would like to know what is happening. Please counsel him.
- ✓ A 13-year-old boy has been having seizures at home. He has come to hospital for an MRI scan but it turns out that he is claustrophobic. Please counsel him appropriately.

Top tips from our mentors

These stations require you to engage with an actor in a role-play. You will be given a brief scenario but don't expect lots of detail. Generally you have quite a lot of license to go where the situation takes you. Try not to look at the invigilator and direct all of your communication towards the actor. Remember that the points are for your communication skills; it doesn't really matter if you say things that aren't entirely accurate, but try to be as professional as possible.

What they want to know

What they want to know might seem obvious – can you communicate with an actor in a role-play? There are some points that you need to be aware of though. Communication generally includes 'empathy', 'active listening' and is often referred to as 'effective' (or not). To demonstrate empathy you have to acknowledge difficult issues from the actor's perspective and state this out loud. For example, use phrases such as 'I appreciate that this is a difficult situation for you', in order to get points for demonstrating empathy. Interjecting appropriately and exploring important issues could demonstrate active listening. Sometimes it is enough to nod, agree, smile and make appropriate eye contact. You could also ask a patient to repeat a significant comment and develop this with them. The measure of effective communication in these situations is whether the mock patient (or parent) feels well counselled or agrees that you have appropriately addressed their concerns. They may still refuse to go ahead with a procedure, but if they have capacity and if you have counselled them appropriately on the options, then this is still a positive result. Refer back to the ethics interview question and part 1 of this guide for more details. There is also a chapter about communicating with patients in the MASTERCLASS guide, that you may find useful.

What you need to write, do or say

Introduce yourself and explain why you are there. Make sure you allow the actor time to introduce him or herself and to explain what is worrying them. Don't forget to employ the active listening techniques as mentioned and try to illicit their main concerns. Explore these issues by asking the actor to provide some reasoned justifications – they will have these prepared. In theses cases you should summarise the actor's main concerns and compare them to the importance of the procedure or treatment, with a summary of benefits. Alternatively you could summarise why they have to wait or what their options are. Your endpoint (and measure of effective communication) is when the patient either agrees or declines to proceed with treatment. Alternatively if there is no treatment available, the endpoint is when they feel that their concerns have been addressed appropriately and they have no more questions. Occasionally the invigilator will question you if there is enough time.

Counselling is something that doctors do regularly. It is possible to apply a logical approach to these situations which students are taught about at medical school. Most of it is common sense, but it keeps the conversation organised, and prevents you from missing any salient points. Here is a step-by-step approach to counselling a patient or parent (actor):

1. Introduce yourself and explain who you are. This is an important step to establish trust and rapport.

2. Ask about the patient's **ideas, concerns and expectations**, (a system referred to as ICE in medicine). This is easily done by asking the patient, "is there anything that I

can help with?" followed by, "is there anything in particular which you are worried about?" At this point in the conversation, the patient should be doing most of the talking and you should be listening. You will be marked on your body language (eye contact etc.) and ability to listen. You will be marked down for interrupting a patient or dismissing any concerns that they have, (even if they seem silly to you). Good listening skills includes picking up on verbal cues. An example of a verbal cue is demonstrated below:

Actor: "Will the test take very long doctor? I don't want to be away from home for too long". *This is a cue to explore this concern further.*

Student: "Is there something that you need to do at home?"

Actor: "My son is not very well and I have to be home to make sure that he has eaten something".

If you had missed this cue, you would not know that there was an unwell child, waiting at home alone.

3. Before you launch into an explanation it is a good idea to find out what the patient already knows about the situation. This gives you more information to appreciate what they already understand, enabling you to fill in the gaps. If this step is missed out, you run the risk of being patronising, by explaining things that the patient already knows.
4. Address the patient's concerns with an explanation. Sometimes this comes in the form of reassurance or encouragement. This is the stage where you start to do more of the talking. By this point you have gathered a lot of information about your patient and will start to appreciate how to talk to them, using language that they understand. Try to avoid medical jargon and keep things simple.
5. It is often good practise to summarise what you have told them, to make sure that you are on the 'same page'. In some situations, it may be better to prompt the patient to summarise what they have understood. You can do this by using phrases such as, "would you like to explain to me what you have understood?"

6. In order to ensure that you have addressed all of their concerns, keep revisiting their ideas, concerns and expectations until the actor is satisfied. They will usually make a statement such as, "thank you for addressing all of my concerns", which will prompt you to finish off the conversation.
7. A nice way to round things off is to offer them a leaflet or direct them to a website where they can find more information. It is courteous to thank the patient and explain that they can come back to you if they have any further questions.

Your turn – write your answer here

Scenario: *A 60-year-old woman has been waiting in A&E for 3 hours. She asks to speak to a doctor, as she wants to know what is happening. She is 3rd in line to be seen. She has had a head injury, is fully mobile and keen to go home. You know that she is not safe to leave until a doctor has reviewed her CT brain scan because she takes a blood-thinning tablet. This puts her at risk of developing a bleed in the brain after a head injury. Explore her concerns and counsel her appropriately.*

Concern 1: How much longer will I have to wait?

Your response:

Concern 2: I need to go home now, as I am the sole carer for my husband with dementia.

Your response:

Concern 3: Why does a doctor need to review my scan if I feel fine and all of my other tests are normal?

Your response

Concern 4: I can't be here because people die in hospitals and I'm worried that I will catch MRSA.

Your response:

Concern 5: Why is that drunken person on a stretcher being seen first despite coming in after me?

Your response:

Concern 6: I am diabetic and I have just self-administered my insulin. I need to eat soon otherwise I will become hypoglycaemic.

Your response:

Interview Skills Checklist (inspired by university mark schemes)

Assessment Areas	Very poor	Poor	Below average	Average	Above average	Very good	Excellent	Points
Introduces self and sets the scene								
Invites actor to discuss concerns with open questions								
Demonstrates active listening and empathy								
Identifies and develops main concerns								
Provides appropriate counselling, support or solutions								
Overall quality of reflections								

Points total	Percentage Score	Passing score
/42	**%**	**>80% *or* 34/42**

Rating	Very poor	Poor	Below average	Average	Above average	Very good	Excellent
Points awarded	**1**	**2**	**3**	**4**	**5**	**6**	**7**

MMI stations: personal statement, skills and experiences – verbal questions

Typical MMI stations that come under this topic

- ✓ Talk me through an example from your personal statement where you demonstrated leadership.
- ✓ You have commented upon your teaching ability, how have you maintained these skills?
- ✓ Do you have an example of developing skills relevant to medicine that is not in your statement?
- ✓ You have recorded a good range of experiences; how will you develop your skills further?

Top tips from our mentors

This MMI station should be home territory as it is all about you. You need to know your personal statement like the back of your hand. The station is essentially a combination of the 'work experience' and 'transferrable skills' sections that appear in traditional interviews. You should expect multiple questions ranging from simple clarification of facts to requests for detailed reflections on skills. You should also expect a few 'curveball' questions; like in the traditional interviews. A classic approach is to push you beyond your statement and request examples of skills or experiences that have not been included. Common sense dictates that you have a few reflections held in reserve for this purpose.

What they want to know

They want to know that you have a wide-ranging and high-quality set of work experiences that are representative of a career in medicine. They want to see appropriate reflection and identification of transferrable skills. Essentially they need to see evidence that you have informed yourself about medicine, tested your own suitability, and then started refining and preparing yourself for the challenges of medical school.

What you need to write, do or say

Answer their questions directly. Make sure you provide them with clear and specific examples so that they can easily tick their checklists. It is vital that you structure your answers using a logical model. Borton's model is great for recounting experiences at interview as it is shorter than Gibbs' model (which is good for personal statements, where more time is available). Detail **what** you did, the significance of your actions (**so what**), and what it means for you as a candidate for medicine (**now what**).

Example question and answer from our mentors

Question: Talk me through an example from your personal statement where you demonstrated leadership

Answer: *I demonstrated leadership skills when I lead my Gold Duke of Edinburgh Award team in our orienteering challenge* ***(question directly answered)****. I organised my teammates into subgroups and designated responsibilities such as tent construction, map reading and food supply monitoring. I drew up a detailed itinerary for our teacher before we set off* ***(what)****. Our team successfully reached its goal, with all team members arriving at the designated map coordinates, in record time* ***(so what).*** *I feel that the leadership, communication and delegation skills I utilised here are highly applicable to a career in medicine. For example when surgeons lead their theatre teams and clearly communicate tasks in a high-pressure environment* ***(now what).***

Your turn – write your answer here

Question: *Do you have an example of developing skills relevant to medicine that is not in your statement? (Answer formatted according to Gibb's reflective cycle)*

Description (what you did):

Feelings (how you felt):

Evaluation (what was good and bad):

Analysis (what sense you made from the experience):

Conclusions:

Action plan and link to medicine:

Question: *You have commented upon your teaching ability; how have you maintained these skills? (Answer formatted according to Borton's model).*

What? (Describe what you did):

So what? (Explain the significance of your actions in relation to a career in medicine):

Now what? (Discuss future plans and skills development):

Interview Skills Checklist (inspired by university mark schemes)

Assessment Areas	Very poor	Poor	Below average	Average	Above average	Very good	Excellent	Points
Answers questions directly								
Provides appropriate work experience examples								
Identifies transferrable skills								
Evidence of continuing professional development								
Demonstrates applicability to a career in medicine								
Overall quality of reflections								

Points total	Percentage Score	Passing score
/42	**%**	**>80% *or* 34/42**

Rating	Very poor	Poor	Below average	Average	Above average	Very good	Excellent
Points awarded	**1**	**2**	**3**	**4**	**5**	**6**	**7**

MMI stations: situational judgement testing – logical decisions, limited information

General information

There are different approaches to situational judgement testing but you can think of it as an applied or facilitated ethical scenario. For these stations, you will normally be given a scenario and then four or five potential actions that you have to rank in order of appropriateness. You will score marks for the most appropriate answers being selected but also for your logical reasoning and justifications – so make sure to state these clearly and out loud. You should expect to receive an initial scenario. This will be added to with new pieces of information. At each stage of the process, you will either be asked to rank the appropriateness of actions taken, or you will need to suggest appropriate actions yourself. You may also be asked to reconsider your previous standpoints in light of the new information or evidence.

Other variable approaches include being given a large range of optional responses for a scenario and being asked to only select a small number of appropriate ones. This can be easier, because you do not have to judge each option – you can class them discretely as appropriate or inappropriate. There is also a third method by which you are asked rank four or five options in order, in response to a more detailed scenario. This differs to the multistage evolving one above. Here again you will be asked to rank action responses from 'always appropriate' to 'always inappropriate' (or an equivalent ranking system). SJT's are becoming increasingly used in MMIs, and the UKCAT now includes an SJT section. For this reason we have given you examples of all three SJT approaches described above.

Typical MMI stations that come under this topic

Practice example 1: You notice that your FY2 colleague regularly takes her jobs list home with her as you have seen her putting it into her handbag. You know that this list contains confidential patient information. Today you found her jobs list on the ground in the hospital car park. Grade the responses as below:

*Always appropriate **(AA)**, Appropriate **(A)** Inappropriate **(I)** Always inappropriate **(AI)***

1) Hand the list back to her and tell her to make nothing of it – these things happen.
2) Hand the list in to the ward sister and let her confront your colleague tomorrow.
3) Ignore the list and inform your consultant line manager as patient confidentiality is at risk.
4) Put the list safely on the ward and chat confidentially with your colleague the next day.

Practice example 2: These four examples are about relationships in a GP practice. There are multiple linked scenarios with rankings from always appropriate to always inappropriate.

Scenario part 1: A GP has had their first consultation with a new patient. At the end of the consultation, the patient invites the GP to go on a date with her, and he accepts. How appropriate is this action? Justify your answers clearly and out loud using logic and reason.

Select your response and justify your points:

1) Always appropriate
2) Usually appropriate
3) Usually inappropriate
4) Always inappropriate

Scenario part 2: The same GP has been a patient's doctor for 30 years and knows their family well. He meets this patient while shopping in the village store. The patient mentions a charity event at the local community centre, and the GP agrees to attend and support the charity. How appropriate is this action? Justify your answers clearly and out loud using logic and reason.

Select your response and justify your points:

1) Always appropriate
2) Usually appropriate

3) Usually inappropriate
4) Always inappropriate

Scenario part 3: A new patient has registered at the GP practice. This patient was previously in a relationship with one of the doctors and now finds herself in a consultation with him. How appropriate is this situation? Justify your answers clearly and out loud, using logic and reason.

Select your response and justify your points:

1) Always appropriate
2) Usually appropriate
3) Usually inappropriate
4) Always inappropriate

Scenario part 4: One of the new medical students on placement at the practice is in a relationship with one of the practice nurses but he does not disclose this information. How appropriate is this situation? Justify your answers clearly and out loud using logic and reason.

Select your response and justify your points:

1) Always appropriate
2) Usually appropriate
3) Usually inappropriate
4) Always inappropriate

Practice example 3: Your hospital is at the centre of a media scandal surrounding A&E waiting times. You answer the phone on the ward and it is a reporter asking for comments. What would you do in this situation? You have five response options. Rearrange them into ranked order from most to least appropriate.

a) Put the phone down straight away before saying anything else.
b) Decline to comment, as you are not able to divulge hospital information over the phone.
c) Provide your opinion on the A&E service at your hospital.
d) Decline to comment and direct the reporter to the hospital's 'media relations' department.
e) Have a lengthy discussion with the reporter about the burden on UK A&E departments.

Ranked 1st:
Ranked 2nd:
Ranked 3rd:
Ranked 4th:
Ranked 5th:

Practice example 4: You are one of two FY1s working on a busy medical ward. After the ward round your colleague says she feels unwell with a headache and thinks she should go home. You are aware that she has not been performing at her best over the past week and that she has not really been engaging with the ward round this morning. Choose 3 appropriate response options and identify 3 inappropriate response options.

*Appropriate **(A)**, Inappropriate **(I)***

Option 1: Tell your colleague that she has a duty of care to her patients and should remain at work.
Option 2: Suggest that she leave immediately as she is clearly unwell and will be of no use.
Option 3: Chat to your colleague privately about how she is feeling.
Option 4: Suggest that she inform her line manager if she is expecting to take time off work.
Option 5: Discuss her case with other colleagues to see if she really looks as ill as she says she is.
Option 6: Cover her jobs until the rota coordinator can arrange replacement cover.

What they want to know

Situational judgement testing channels your reason and logic into categorical decisions. This makes it easier to mark from a checklist perspective. This station essentially covers all of the same areas as ethical and legal interview questions. In addition to grading the appropriateness of available responses you have to show your working. This is particularly important when you have to rank responses in order of appropriateness. You will find that some response options are clearly appropriate or inappropriate. It can be more difficult with borderline responses or different options that seem similar. If you mention how you have ranked options aloud then you engage the interviewer and occasionally they may prompt you by asking you to 'look at the option again' or other words to that effect. They may not do this but if you do not share your reasoning you are excluding them from the process and you may miss out on some of the available scoring points.

What you need to write, do or say

In an MMI station, time is clearly limited. You should take an organised approach and investigate each response option before moving on to the next. Generally speaking, the most appropriate options are the ones that **maintain patient safety**, **prevent harm (to colleagues and patients)** and are likely to be in the **patient's (and colleagues') best interests.** Inappropriate options are unlikely to address (or they may actively work against) these concepts. They are also likely to be disproportionate, illogical, **disrespect autonomy** or even illegal – remember **justice** is also an ethical principal. Make sure you are familiar with contemporary healthcare ethics and fundamental principles. Refer back to the ethical topic in part 3b of this guide.

Situational Judgement Testing Practice Example Answers

Practice example 1

1) Hand the list back to her and tell her to make nothing of it – these things happen.
Inappropriate*. The initial patient safety issue is addressed but there is further risk of patients' confidential details being exposed to the public.*

2) Hand the list in to the ward sister and let her confront your colleague tomorrow.
Inappropriate. *The initial patient safety issue is addressed but your actions constitute an arguably unnecessary escalation of the issue outside of your own profession.*

3) Ignore the list and inform your consultant line manager as patient confidentiality is at risk.
Always inappropriate. *Even though you have acknowledged the need to act to preserve patient confidentiality, your initial inaction has contravened this very issue.*

4) Put the list safely on the ward and chat confidentially with your colleague the next day.
Always appropriate. *You have dealt with the initial confidentiality issue appropriately. You have also formulated a reasonable plan to prevent further issues arising. Confidentially addressing your colleague is a respectful way to approach the situation as it maintains their dignity and gives them the opportunity to improve their practice. If they were not fully appreciative of the issue then you would be within your rights to approach a senior doctor – ideally their educational or clinical supervisors.*

Practice example 2

Scenario part 1: It is ***always inappropriate*** *for a GP to accept a social engagement of this kind as it can compromise objectivity in the doctor-patient relationship.*

Scenario part 3: It is ***usually appropriate*** *for a GP to attend community events such as this. Occasionally it might be inadvisable for a GP to attend a small event where many of their patients might be present.*

Scenario part 3: It is ***always inappropriate*** *for a GP to be in this situation. It is unfair on both the patient and the GP and again is likely to compromise objectivity in the doctor-patient relationship.*

Scenario part 4: It is ***usually appropriate*** *for the medical student not to declare his relationship. He has a human right to his private life after all, and patient safety is unlikely to be affected. It would be inappropriate however to ask the nurse to fill out an assessment or* *otherwise provide feedback on his performance as her objectivity is likely to be compromised.*

Practice example 3

Ranked 1st: Decline to comment and direct the reporter to the hospital's 'media relations' department.

This is the best option as it is polite and appropriate.

Ranked 2nd: Decline to comment, as you are not able to divulge hospital information over the phone.

This is also appropriate but slightly less polite or helpful.

Ranked 3rd: Put the phone down straight away before saying anything else.

This is acceptable, as you are not obliged to speak to reporters.

Ranked 4th: Have a lengthy discussion with the reporter about the burden on UK A&E departments.

This is unnecessary and will take you away from clinical duties – patients could suffer as a result.

Ranked 5th: Provide your opinion on the A&E service at your hospital

This is unnecessary, unhelpful and unprofessional. It also takes you away from clinical duties and patients could suffer as a result.

Practice example 4

Option 1: Tell your colleague that she has a duty of care to her patients and should remain at work.

Inappropriate: *She may have a duty of care but it is her decision as to whether she is fit to work. You may be doing harm to your colleague by pressurising her into staying.*

Option 2: Suggest that she leaves immediately as she is clearly unwell and will be of no use.

Inappropriate: *If she leaves straight away and abandons her jobs, you may find it difficult to cope and patient safety may be compromised. It would be worth discussing the issue to see if she can stay at work until emergency cover can be arranged – teamwork and communication are the key here.*

Option 3: Chat privately to your colleague about how she is feeling and find out more about the situation.

Appropriate: *She has divulged how she is feeling to you anyway. If you discuss the issue further you may be able to come to a reasonable arrangement to cover ward tasks in her absence; she may even feel well enough to stay for a few hours until urgent jobs are complete. Again think about teamwork, communication and patient safety.*

Option 4: Suggest that she inform her line manager if she is expecting to take time off work.

Appropriate: *This is a good idea; it will give the rota coordinator and senior doctors enough time to arrange cover. If your colleague remains ill; then she will not feel pressurised into coming back to work early, as cover arrangements are in place.*

Option 5: Discuss her case with other colleagues to see if she really looks as ill as she says she is.

Inappropriate: *This is unfair and harmful to your colleague. She came to you as her medical colleague and would not expect you to divulge this information unnecessarily. You have a duty of care to your colleagues as well. Idle gossip of this kind is not productive.*

Option 6: Cover her jobs until the rota coordinator can arrange replacement cover.

Appropriate: *You have a duty of care to colleagues, the trust and patients. You may have to work a bit harder for a short period of time but doctors are normally contractually obliged to provide emergency cover if rota gaps arise with less than 48 hours notice.*

Interview Skills Checklist (inspired by university mark schemes)

Assessment Areas	Very poor	Poor	Below average	Average	Above average	Very good	Excellent	Points
Makes reasonable choices								
Demonstrates logical reasoning								
Formulates coherent arguments								
Clearly states justifications								
Utilises appropriate theory to support points								
Overall quality of reflections								

Points total	Percentage Score	Passing score
/42	%	**>80% *or* 34/42**

Rating	Very poor	Poor	Below average	Average	Above average	Very good	Excellent
Points awarded	**1**	**2**	**3**	**4**	**5**	**6**	**7**

Example MMI station for this topic

In this station, you will be given a written source of information, and a few minutes to read it and then answer questions. Information sources often include: magazine and scientific journal articles, news articles, GMC and other health-related documents. For example, you are given a magazine article excerpt, written by a medical student and detailing their advocacy of problem-based learning over the traditional subject and lecture based medical curriculum. You are given 2 minutes to read the document and asked the questions detailed below:

- ✓ Summarise the key points of the article?
- ✓ What are the pros and cons of the argument being put forward?
- ✓ How reliable is this article as an information source?
- ✓ Are there more reliable sources of information out there?

Problem-based learning (PBL) is the latest evolutionary stage of the UK undergraduate medical curriculum. It is the only true interpretation of a fully integrated curriculum. That is a teaching structure that fully integrates early patient contact and theoretical study, practical skills and sciences fundamental to medicine. Unlike traditional curricula, which only permit lectures and anatomy-based teaching for the first two (pre-clinical) years, PBL students are able to greatly develop their communication, empathy and interpersonal skills. In addition to this, reducing contact time and placing students into self-directed PBL groups, forces them to apply team-working, leadership and initiative. It is my belief the PBL course at my medical school has made me into the balanced, resourceful and compassionate student that I am today.

Joe Bloggs, 5th year medical student

Key points: This is a descriptive article, based upon personal experience. It states that PBL curricula are better than traditional ones by referring to opportunities to develop specific transferrable skills. A 5th year medical student has written it.

Pros and cons: The article provides a unique insight into the personal experiences of a medical student. It is more credible than somebody commenting from outside the course. The author refers to several transferrable skills that strengthen his argument. His explanation for the development of interpersonal skills through patient contact is logical. Working in groups with minimal direction would also logically lead to the development of team-working skills and personal initiative. He refers only to his own medical school curriculum and compares it to a generic 'traditional' curriculum. He provides no evidence from other courses and there are no other commentators to provide opposing anecdotes. In this excerpt at least, he has not provided a balanced argument by considering the benefits of traditional curricula or the drawbacks of PBL. His conclusions are all drawn from subjective experience and may not therefore be wholly representative of the differences between current medical school curricula and teaching methods.

Reliability: This excerpt is purely anecdotal as it is unreferenced, contains no hypothesis, research question or scientific methodology. It is therefore ranked lowest in the hierarchy of scientific of evidence. It could be made more reliable by the addition of any of the above points, as well as additional commentators and more detailed descriptions of undergraduate course structures. A peer-review process would likely reject this article for a scientific journal, but it could be a useful opinion piece for a student magazine.

Practice example: A journal article abstract

- ✓ Is there a hypothesis or research question?
- ✓ What type of study is this?
- ✓ What are the key findings?
- ✓ What are the main conclusions?
- ✓ What problems are addressed?
- ✓ Was this a worthwhile study?

Finals Revision Programme (FRP) is an exciting, effective and innovative peer-assisted learning programme. The course is entirely organised and delivered by trainee doctors and incorporates a virtual mentoring scheme, mobile and web technologies. This makes FRP an interactive programme that utilises modern technology and employs 'distance-learning', which is increasingly needed as medical students spend more time on placement, away from the University. In 2013, it involved over 75 FY1 doctors and nearly 600 medical students. Feedback was obtained via questionnaires; students were given these pre-course and post-course, in addition to individual lecture questionnaires. The lecturers were also invited to complete a post-lecture questionnaire. 93% of students believed that FRP was an integral part of their revision, and 94% of students would recommend the programme to other students. 89% of students also felt that FRP helped them to prepare for work as an FY1 doctor. From FY1 feedback, 86% believed that it helped to improve their teaching and presentation skills. 97% have uploaded their FRP certificates, 83% have reflected on their teaching experience, 90% have uploaded their student feedback sheets and 38% have used FRP to complete the 'clinical teacher assessment'. Most importantly, 100% of FY1 doctors would recommend FRP to other junior doctors. Peer assisted learning can be useful in preparing medical students for exams and for work. The feedback shows that there are several benefits to both the students and lecturers.

Your turn – write your answers here

Top tips from our mentor

This station requires you to be familiar with basic *critical appraisal* techniques. Some of you will have studied critical thinking in schools. Analysing scientific articles is similar but has a specific focus upon scientific methodology and study design. With a descriptive piece of writing such as the 'student experience' in the example, you can use a more generic approach. Gibbs' and Borton's reflective models can be of use here. You will find that some of the questions (or tasks in this case) are quite straight forward 'summarise the key points' or, 'comment upon the transferrable skills used'. These are not new concepts. Alternatively you may be asked more probing questions such as, 'how reliable is this source' or 'are there more reliable sources available?' You do need to be familiar with basic scientific research concepts such as the *hierarchy of evidence* and what a *peer-reviewed journal* article is. Your knowledge does not need to be highly detailed however. A good place to start is the MASTERCLASS application guide, which has a chapter on research methods.

What they want to know

For this station, you have to demonstrate an understanding of basic argument structure. This could range from a descriptive argument to a scientific hypothesis and research question, with results, conclusions and a discussion. You may also be given some basic data tables or graphs and be asked to draw your own conclusions. You should be aware of the limitations of data and the value of different sources; say what you see and also what you think it means. If you can think of alternative arguments or even a better scientific test, then you will appear well rounded. You should always aim to explore both sides of an argument by analysing and evaluating its positives and negatives. This is why a reflective model comes in very handy.

Interview Skills Checklist (inspired by university mark schemes)

Assessment Areas	Very poor	Poor	Below average	Average	Above average	Very good	Excellent	Points
Answers questions directly								
Identification of source material								
Analysis and understanding of source material								
Evaluation of strengths and weaknesses								
Evaluation of usefulness and reliability								
Overall quality of reflections								

Points total	Percentage Score	Passing score
/42	%	>80% *or* 34/42

Rating	Very poor	Poor	Below average	Average	Above average	Very good	Excellent
Points awarded	**1**	**2**	**3**	**4**	**5**	**6**	**7**

Final Points

Preparation

The key to being successful at interview is to practice. Finding time to do this is always challenging around 'interview season' because of exams, coursework and other school and personal commitments. If you have got this guide early and read through it over the summer, then you are already well ahead. Most students have the approach that they will start preparing only once they have been invited to interview. If you have read the medical applications guides, attended the courses, done your research, met the entry requirements and have a good reference – you will probably be called for at least one interview. There is no harm in preparing some small things early. For example, you can organise your research on the GMC, NICE and other organisations in advance and prepare some model answers in this book over the summer. These things take up the most time.

Communication skills

A lot of this book has focused on interview questions. Remember that there are other important aspects of interview technique, which you need to master: verbal and non-verbal communication. You can improve these skills by practicing regularly and also by attending the Interview Skills Course where a lot of this will be taught in detail.

The night before the interview

The night before the interview, do your best to relax and get some sleep. This is important because sleep deprivation will have an impact on your performance. Try to wake up reasonably early and not leave things to the last minute. Your nerves are likely to start kicking in from the moment you get up and in this heightened state you are at risk of forgetting and misplacing things. Therefore, prepare your interview clothes, documents, train tickets and venue details at least the day before. It is often a good idea to iron 2 shirts, just in case you need it. Decide on simple things such as who is going to drop you off and pick you up in advance. This prevents any early morning disagreements!

On the day of the interview

You are going to feel nervous and that is normal. Sometimes pretending not to be nervous will actually help you to feel less so. Remembering to smile will make the biggest difference. Many candidates don't smile at interviewers and it is refreshing to see someone who does. It also has a positive impact on the interviewer, particularly when it comes down to marking the 'overall impression' component of the mark scheme. If you look as though you have enjoyed being interviewed then the interviewer will mark this positively.

In timed MMI stations, you will feel a lot of pressure to try and say as much as you can. This will actually work against you. It is easy to start automatically listing things in an attempt to cram everything in. Try to forget that there is a buzzer, but remember to be concise and avoid waffle. Even if the bell does ring in the middle of your sentence, calmly finish it and thank the interviewers.

Refuse to let anything fluster you. This is a mindset. Do not expect to be prepared for every possible question and then nothing will surprise you. If you are asked a question and the answer is not obvious straight away, just apply some common sense to the problem. Utilize aspects of your prepared answers and construct an organised logical response. If you feel that an MMI station has gone badly, do not let it ruin the rest of your interview. This is easier said than done, but it is important.

We wish you the best of luck with your interviews and keep in touch if there is anything else that you need help with.

-Medic Mentor Team

Further reading and references

1. Rolfe, G., Freshwater, D., Jasper, M. (2001) Critical reflection in nursing and the helping professions: a user's guide. Basingstoke: Palgrave Macmillan

2. Gibbs, G., 1988. Learning by Doing: A Guide to Teaching and Learning Methods. Oxford Further Education Unit, Oxford.

3. Borton, T. (1970) Reach, Touch and Teach. London: Hutchinson

4. Tomorrow's Doctors 2009. Published by the General Medical Council and available online at: http://www.gmc-uk.org/Tomorrow_s_Doctors_1214.pdf_48905759.pdf

5. Modernising Medical Careers (MMC) was a major reform that began in August 2005. It was a reshuffle of postgraduate training and began with the introduction of the Foundation Training Programme in 2005. There are differences in MMC implementation in England, Scotland, Wales and Northern Ireland. Modernising Medical Careers: final report. Tony Delamothe. BMJ. 2008 Jan 12; 336(7635): 54–55.

6. Good Medical Practice was published by the General Medical Council in 2013 and this has been updated on the 29th April 2014. You can find it online here: http://www.gmc-uk.org/static/documents/content/Good_medical_practice_-_English_0914.pdf

7. National Institute for Clinical Excellence (NICE) website: www.nice.org.uk

8. General Medical Council (GMC): www.gmc-uk.org

9. British Medical Association (BMA): bma.org.uk

10. Public Health England: https://www.gov.uk/government/organisations/public-health-england/about

11. Find our about Medic Mentor's prizes, publishing opportunities and the Excellence Award at www.medicmentor.org

Best of luck!